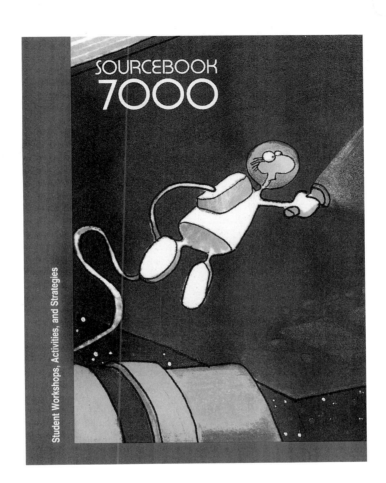

SOURCEBOOK
7000

Student Workshops, Activities, and Strategies

*. . . a resource of student
workshops, activities, and
strategies to accompany*

WRITE SOURCE
2000

A FEW WORDS ABOUT SOURCEBOOK 7000

■ **Below are some of the people who developed your SourceBook.**

Authors: Pat Sebranek,
Dave Kemper,
Randall VanderMey

Contributing Teachers:
Pat Andrews,
Laura Bachman,
Gina Camodeca,
Carol Elsholz,
Candice Fortmann,
Tom Gilding,
Mary Gregory,
Janis Hartley,
Phyllis Jaeger,
Bev Jessen,
Bonnie Knoblauch,
Dale Ann Morgan,
Peg Rifken,
V. Kelly Saaf,
Pat Santilli,
Cynthia Stock,
Betsy Watson

Editor: Lois Krenzke
Graphics: Sherry Gordon
Illustrator: Chris Krenzke

Before you begin . . .

it is important for you to know that your *SourceBook 7000* must be used with the *Write Source 2000 Handbook*. The handbook provides guidelines, examples, and models; the *SourceBook* provides many opportunities to put that information into practice. It's also important for you to know how all of the activities in the *SourceBook* are organized.

Part I contains seven core writing units that address many of the important forms of writing covered in the handbook, including autobiographical and biographical writing, paragraphs, essays, and stories.

Part II contains many different workshop activities that will help you at all stages of the writing process, from prewriting to proofreading.

Part III contains language workshops that will help you better understand how words work, and learning workshops that will help you become a better thinker, study-reader, speaker, and listener.

Part IV, way in the back of the book, features a series of minilessons that relate to all of the different areas of writing, language, and learning covered in your handbook.

What makes "shopping" in your *SourceBook* so worthwhile is that the activities come in so many different shapes and sizes; there is something to please everybody. All you and your teacher have to do is decide what units and workshops best meet your needs. We're sure that all of your shopping experiences in this *SourceBook* will help you improve as a writer and as a learner.

Published simultaneously in Canada

Printed in the United States of America

International Standard Book Number: 0-669-38622-7

3 4 5 6 7 8 9 10 -RRDW- 00 99 98 97 96 95

TABLE OF CONTENTS

Part I: Core Writing Units

Part II: Writing Workshops

Part III: Language and Learning Workshops

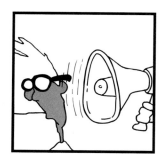

Part IV: Writing and Learning Minilessons

PART I
Core Writing Units

OBSERVING AND RECORDING

Writing from Start to Finish

The **Core Writing Units** provide you with a series of seven extended writing activities addressing many of the basic types of writing covered in the *Write Source 2000* student handbook: autobiographical writing, paragraphs, essays, and stories. As you complete your work in these units, you will be gaining valuable experience with the types of writing tasks you are often asked to carry out in your classes, as well as in most writing assessment tests. You will also be practicing the very skills that are at the "core" of the writing process, from selecting subjects to correcting final drafts.

It's important to know that everything you need to complete your work is included, from step-by-step guidelines to student models. In addition, each page within these units is self-contained, providing you with clearly identifiable starting and stopping points for your work. This will make it easy for you to stay on task from one day to the next. Upon completion of each unit, you will have produced at least one important piece of writing.

User's Checklist

Check your progress as you work on these **Core Writing Units.**

☐ **Writing About Personal Experiences**
School Days

☐ **Building Paragraphs: Part 1**
Reviewing and Using Supporting Details

☐ **Building Paragraphs: Part 2**
Using Planning Strategies

☐ **Writing a Character Sketch**
She led a "storied" life.

☐ **Writing Myths**
It's all Greek to me . . .

☐ **Writing About Problems and Solutions**
You think you've got problems!

☐ **Writing a Report**
If I were a carpenter or a dentist . . .

FOLLOW-UP • Does your teacher expect you to turn in a writing portfolio at the end of the grading period? If so, reserve some space in it for the writing you complete in these units.

WRITING ABOUT PERSONAL EXPERIENCES

School Days

(fore•words) Autobiographical writing gives you the opportunity to explore and share memorable experiences from your past. It's important to write autobiographical papers openly and honestly, to let the real you shine through in your work. By writing in this way, you'll be more likely to uncover long-forgotten ideas and form richer and deeper understandings. Plus, the results of your efforts, your writing, will be much more entertaining and lively to read.

Remember: To write well, whether you are sharing a personal story or compiling a report, you must be able to "speak" in an honest and natural voice.

READ: As you read Sarah Klafka's model writing, watch for key words or phrases that help make this experience come alive.

> As I walked slowly down the hallway, it seemed as if it would last for miles. My heart pounded, and, although sweat poured down my face, I felt a cold chill within. Other students stared at me to such a degree that I felt as if I was being inspected. Too scared to introduce myself to anyone, I hurried down to the room at the end of the hall. In the corner desk by myself, I sat . . . alone without a friend in the world. Until . . . out of the corner of my eye, a figure drew closer. Still too nervous to speak, I pretended not to notice her. But then she spoke, "Hi, my name is Kelly. Are you new?" Suddenly my anxiety decreased. I felt calm and relaxed, more like I belonged. I answered Kelly and our conversation continued. I had met my first friend in my new school.

REACT: Use the following questions to help you react to this model.

- What do you like best about this writing?
- Does the writing present a clear picture of this experience?
- What would you have done differently?
- Does this model remind you of any school-related experiences from your past?

(after•words) For another model, refer to "Writing, About experiences" in the handbook index. Respond to the handbook model using the **REACT** questions above. Also, decide how the handbook model compares to the one on this page. (Share your responses.)

■ Recalling a Difficult Moment

Look, Mom, no hands!

WRITE: Have you ever watched someone do something and thought that it looked sooooo easy? Then you tried and failed, and wondered how something could look so easy and be so difficult? Recall such a moment related to school life, and complete the autobiographical sketch below.

One day, when I was _____ , I decided to _____ .

It looked so easy. I thought all you would have to do was _____

_____

Boy, was I mistaken. Let me tell you how wrong I was . . . _____

_____

_____

_____

_____

_____

_____

_____

_____

(after•words) Share your writing with a classmate, and find out what she or he likes about it. Next, carefully review your work yourself to see if you agree with your partner's comments. Then make all the necessary changes to your writing until it "works" for you from start to finish.

■ Gathering Ideas for Additional Writing: Clustering

(fore•words) There are many prewriting strategies that will help you gather ideas for writing assignments. One of the most effective gathering strategies is **clustering**. To cluster, you write a general word or phrase (nucleus word) related to your assignment in the middle of a blank sheet of paper. You then record every word or idea that comes to mind when you think of the nucleus word. Each new idea is circled and connected to the closest related word.

➤ *Now You Try*

CLUSTER: For your next autobiographical writing, gather possible writing ideas by completing a cluster around *early school experiences*. See how many ideas you can cluster in 5 minutes.

HANDBOOK HELPER	Before you start your work, refer to "Clustering" in the index for an example. (Notice how related ideas are connected.)

Early School Experiences

(after•words) Share your work with a classmate. Compare the different types of information each of you recorded. Then, put a ✔ next to one idea in your cluster that you would like to explore in writing.

■ **Responding to a "Clustered" Idea in Writing**

Close Inspection

WRITE: Write nonstop for 5-10 minutes about the idea you checked at the end of the last activity. (Have another piece of paper ready in case you run out of room here.)

Helpful Hint: Make sure this idea is one that really interests you, one that you would like to explore further.

_____

_____

_____

_____

_____

_____

_____

_____

_____

_____

_____

_____

_____

_____

(after•words) Carefully review your writing. If your free writing focuses on one experience, consider it a first draft of your next autobiographical paper, and decide what additional details you would like to include. If your writing jumped around a bit (which is okay), look for a reference to a specific experience that could serve as the subject for your paper. Then think about how you would like to write about this experience.

■ Understanding Personal Details

Give me the "dets."

(fore•words) Because you are writing about a personal experience, you have a good knowledge base. This will make your job much easier when it comes to including personal details in your writing.

Personal details fall into three general categories: *sensory* details (seeing, hearing, tasting, etc.), *memory* details (remembering), and *reflective* details (wondering and wishing). *To help readers fully appreciate your autobiographical writing, make sure you include a lot of memory and sensory details.*

HANDBOOK HELPER Refer to "Details, Kinds of" in the index for more information.

READ & REACT: The eight sentences below contain personal details. Put an S in front of the sentences containing sensory details, an M in front of sentences containing memory details, and an R in front of sentences containing reflective details.

Example: __M__ When I was small, Popsicles were only a nickel.

_____ 1. I'll never forget the shocked look on Aunt Irene's face.

_____ 2. The familiar smell of hot dogs and beans made me hungry.

_____ 3. What was there to do for fun before video games?

_____ 4. A beautiful pot of red geraniums hung above the entrance.

_____ 5. Miss Mandez always praised us for working hard.

_____ 6. I wish I could go to New Mexico again someday.

_____ 7. I wonder where my old friend Jerome is living now.

_____ 8. In a matter of seconds, the sand grilled the bottoms of my feet.

REVIEW: Now review your first autobiographical writing in this unit ("Look, Mom, no hands!") or another piece of writing for examples of personal details. Label examples with an S, M, or R. This review will give you some idea of the quality and quantity of detail in your writing.

Special Challenge: Find a newspaper or magazine article containing effective details to share with your classmates. Be able to tell them what types of details (S, M, or R) are emphasized.

■ Collecting Personal Details for Writing

COLLECTING: Gather some memory and sensory details for your writing by filling in the "Personal Detail Checklist" below.

Special Note: If you've already completed a first draft (after the clustering activity), some of the ideas you list here will help you improve upon your work as you revise.

Personal Detail Checklist

Memory Details   (At a minimum, you should be able to answer the 5 W's about your experience.)

who? *(Who was involved in this experience?)* _____

_____

what? *(What happened?)* _____

_____

when? and **where?** _____

why? _____

_____

how? *(For better coverage)* _____

_____

Sensory Details   (Think of the sights, sounds, etc., that you want to emphasize. But don't force these details; not all of the senses will come into play.)

sights _____

_____

sounds _____

_____

smells, tastes, and textures _____

_____

_____

■ **Planning and Writing Your Paper**

Connecting All of Your Thoughts

(fore•words) Before you begin (or continue) your writing, make sure you know what main feeling or impression you want to share with your readers. Do you want to entertain them because your experience is humorous? Or do you want your readers to feel a sense of fear, anger, pride, surprise, or understanding when they read your paper?

Let this feeling be your guide as you develop your paper. Every detail that you include should support this feeling. And the way you express yourself, the special way you say things, should reflect and support this feeling as well.

WRITE: Connect all of your thoughts about your subject by writing a first draft. Make sure to include many of the personal details that you listed in the previous activity. (Do all of your writing on your own paper.)

Special Note: Don't worry too much about the sound or appearance of your first draft. This is, after all, only your first complete look at your writing idea. You'll have plenty of time later to make improvements.

HANDBOOK HELPER	Refer to "Writing, About experiences" in the index if you need more help with your writing.

EVALUATE: The following checklist will help you review and revise your first draft. (Use this same checklist to evaluate your classmates' work.)

_____ **Organization:** Are all of the details arranged in a clear and logical order, as things happened during this experience?

_____ **Detail:** Are enough details, especially memory and sensory details, provided?

_____ **Style:** Does the writing seem to be focused around a main feeling? Does the writer speak honestly and naturally?

_____ **Mechanics:** Has proper attention been given to neatness and accuracy? (Look for complete sentences, spelling errors, and proper punctuation and grammar.)

(after•words) Share your finished product with your classmates. Everyone likes a good story, especially one related to school life.

■ Writing About an Early Experience

"Or so they tell me."

Is there an event or a time in your life that you "remember" well because someone (grandparent, mother, older sister or brother) has told you about it? You don't actually remember it from firsthand experience, but from all the times the story has been told and retold.

WRITE: Share this event or time in your life in an autobiographical paper. (Use the space provided below for your planning or first draft. Finish your work on your own paper.)

Helpful Hint Some of the events or phases you have experienced may fall into the category of "firsts"—your first word, your first step, your first birthday, your first injury, your first day of school, etc.

(after•words) Share this "secondhand" story with your classmates, friends, and family members.

BUILDING PARAGRAPHS: PART 1

Reviewing and Using Supporting Details

(fore•words) Have you ever wondered why some people can write so much better than others? Part of their secret is their ability to build strong word pictures, pictures which the reader can "see" as he or she reads. Another secret is that most good writing is organized into clear thought groups.

One such thought group is the paragraph. By using paragraphs effectively, you can help move the reader from one idea to the next. A paragraph functions like the human body—several important parts must be there for it to work. One way to remember what a paragraph must do is to develop your own word picture about it. Sooo . . .

READ & COMPLETE: Read the first two pages in "Building Paragraphs." (Refer to "Paragraph" in your handbook index.) Then ask yourself, "What can the three parts of a paragraph be compared to? What are they like?" Complete one of the open-ended sentences below (or come up with one of your own) to build a word picture that describes a paragraph's three working parts.

A paragraph is like a sandwich because _____

_____ .

A paragraph is like a house because _____

_____ .

A paragraph is like a _____ because _____

_____

_____

_____ .

(Your Own Idea) _____

_____

_____

_____ .

DRAW: Draw your "word picture" in the box (or on your own paper) and label the parts of your paragraph word picture. (Share the results of your work with your classmates.)

■ Understanding Topic Sentences

Controlling What You Say

(fore•words) All writing is really a matter of solving a problem. When you begin writing, you won't know how you can solve the problem; but you should at least know what the problem is. You should state clearly, at the very beginning, what it is you are trying to do—what problem it is you are trying to solve. It is, therefore, a good idea to begin each paragraph with a topic sentence which does exactly that—states what "problem" you are trying to solve.

As you discovered when you read about paragraphs in the previous activity, the key to writing a good topic sentence is limiting your problem or subject and making clear your feelings or attitude about it. Here is a simple formula to remember for writing topic sentences:

A specific subject + a specific feeling or attitude =
a good topic sentence.

IDENTIFY: Underline the key words (*subject* and *feeling* or *attitude*) in the following topic sentences. (The first one is done for you.)

1. Erin is a very good friend.

2. Our school library lacks atmosphere.

3. The U2 concert was one of the most unusual I've ever attended.

4. Harold cannot avoid trouble.

5. Mrs. Magnavox inspires us with her oral readings.

6. The badly polluted river saddens me a great deal.

COMPLETE: Fill in the blanks below with words or phrases which will make each sentence a good topic sentence.

1. My good friend amazes me with her ability to _____ .

2. The beach has always been _____ .

3. The first day of school _____ .

4. _____ was an unforgettable experience.

5. I cannot help but laugh every time _____ .

Special Challenge: Put a ✔ next to the topic sentence you like the best, and use it as the starting point for a paragraph.

■ Writing Strong Topic Sentences

A Change for the Better

REWRITE: Change each of the topic sentences below so that a clear subject and a specific feeling or attitude are expressed in each. (Refer to "Paragraph, Topic sentence" in the handbook index for help.)

1. My grandma is very active. *My active grandma amazes me.* (Reworded to

   express a specific feeling or attitude)

2. I remember one certain person from eighth grade. *Roy Baker is one eighth grader*

   I'll never forget. (Reworded to make the sentence more interesting and specific)

3. Uncle Ervin was a very memorable person. _____

   _____

   _____

4. I remember the first time I saw my new seventh-grade English teacher.

   _____

   _____

5. One summer night I went to our new neighbor's house. _____

   _____

   _____

6. Dutchess is our family dog. _____

   _____

7. Yolanda Johnson was one of my friends. _____

   _____

8. In fourth grade I made an art project. _____

   _____

   _____

■ Writing Strong Topic Sentences *(continued)*

CREATE: Write a topic sentence for each of the subjects listed below. Narrow the subject to a topic which can be covered in a single paragraph. Be sure to include a specific subject and a specific feeling or attitude.

1. (a near accident) *I shook for days after my near collision with a delivery truck.*

_____

2. (a memorable teacher) _____

_____

3. (the school library) _____

_____

4. (a game) _____

_____

5. (an old friend) _____

_____

SELECT: Now choose one of the topic sentences above and list at least four details about that topic. (Write your topic sentence on the first line.)

Topic Sentence: _____

_____

_____ detail: _____

_____ detail: _____

_____ detail: _____

_____ detail: _____

_____ detail: _____

(after•words) Review your list of details and arrange them in the best possible order (by location, time, importance, etc.). Simply number your details on the blanks to the left. (Refer to "Arrangement, Of sentences" in the handbook index for help.) Then write a paragraph, working in the details as you have arranged them.

■ **Using Sensory Details**

Observe, Remember, Imagine

(fore•words) A good writer collects details from personal experience. Often, the most true-to-life writing is the strongest. It seems to talk from the memory of the reader as well as the writer.

There are three kinds of personal details: **sensory**, **memory**, and **reflective**. Good writing generally includes all three! This activity will help you recognize and use the sensory details that literally surround you.

LIST: *Sensory details* are gathered through firsthand experience. A good descriptive paragraph can be written about the most common, everyday objects. Hold your pencil (or pen) in your hand. Observe the pencil, using all five senses, and jot down as many ideas as possible under the correct headings below. (Share your observations with your classmates.)

SIGHT
SMELL
SOUND
TASTE
TOUCH

(after•words) Write a sensory paragraph about your pencil (or pen). Use as many of the details from above as you can in your writing. (Refer to the "Building Paragraphs" chapter in your handbook for help.)

■ **Using Memory Details**

How good is your memory?

(fore•words) **Memory details** come when a writer thinks about past experiences and observations. This could include details from last week or five years ago. (Refer to "Memory, details" in the handbook index for more information.)

COMPLETE: **Answer the questions below. Your answers may surprise you by showing how much or how little you remember about daily events.**

1. What did your best friend wear yesterday? _____

   _____

   _____

2. How would you describe the food smells in your kitchen at breakfast this morning? (Don't use the names of the foods in your description unless absolutely necessary.)

   _____

   _____

   _____

3. What is the clearest memory you have involving food (from at least a week ago)?

   _____

   _____

   _____

4. How did the air feel this morning?_____

   _____

5. What was the last noise you heard outside before entering school this morning?

   _____

   _____

Special Challenge: On a separate sheet of paper, write freely and rapidly for 5 minutes about your earliest memories, going back to your toddler years—or even before! (Be prepared to unlock some surprising ideas.)

■ Using Reflective Details

Imagine . . .

(fore•words) In narrative and descriptive writing, the writer often uses his or her imagination to wonder about what could have been or might yet be. These **reflective details** grow out of what you already know, but leave room for you to create or invent. (Refer to "Reflective detail" in the handbook index for more information.)

OBSERVE: Look around your present classroom and follow the instructions below.

1. List items that would not have been in a classroom when your parents were middle-school students.

   _____

   _____

   _____

   _____

2. List items that would not have been in a classroom when your grandparents were students.

   _____

   _____

   _____

   _____

3. List items that might be in a classroom when your children will be in the grade you're in now.

   _____

   _____

   _____

   _____

(after•words) Write a reflective paragraph explaining a typical school day 25 or 40 years ago, or 25 years into the future. (You'll just naturally have to do some reflecting and wondering in your work.)

© 1995 Write Source Educational Publishing House, Box 460, Burlington, WI 53105

BUILDING PARAGRAPHS: PART 2

Using Planning Strategies

(fore•words) As you know, a **paragraph** is a group of sentences having one controlling idea, an idea which is found in the **topic sentence**. The sentences in the **body** of the paragraph prove or develop the controlling idea found in the topic sentence. (Refer to "Paragraph, Basic parts" in your handbook index for more information.)

❏ Below is a brief outline of a paragraph *before* it is turned into detailed sentences. The word "unforgettable" indicates the attitude or feeling that will control the paragraph.

    I. An   *unforgettable*   first day in the country
        A. Seeing a snake
        B. Catching it
        C. Getting bitten
        D. Going to the hospital
        E. Visiting with the doctor

❏ Here is the outline turned into sentences to form a paragraph.

Topic Sentence

    My mom and I will never forget the first day in our new country home. We were sitting in the backyard when we spotted a snake. My mom jumped on the picnic table, but I was too curious for that. I caught the snake by its tail and lifted it up. The snake immediately curved upward and bit me on the thigh. We both screamed and ran into the house. My mom called the poison control center, and, before I knew it, we were on our way to the hospital. As soon as we arrived, we were taken to a young, serious-looking doctor. I was really scared by this time, but I shouldn't have been. The doctor took one look at my bite, put an ice pack on it, and told us I had been bitten by a harmless, nonpoisonous snake. My mom and I just looked at each other and burst out laughing. We had learned our first lesson about country living.

Body

Closing Sentence

Discussion: Details were added during the actual writing to help readers appreciate the experience. The paragraph was brought to an effective stopping point with the **closing sentence**.

PLAN: On your own paper, create a brief outline for a paragraph. The controlling idea of your paragraph outline should be an unforgettable experience.

(after•words) Develop a paragraph from your plan. Begin your paragraph with an effective topic sentence, and end it with a strong closing sentence. Include plenty of good detail in the body.

■ Developing a Four-Step Paragraph

The Four-Step Process

(fore•words) The process of writing a paragraph is really no different from the process of writing a longer composition like a report or an essay. A writer first **selects** an interesting topic and **collects** his or her thoughts about it. After **connecting** these thoughts in a rough draft, and later in revised writings, the writer brings the process to a close by **correcting** the final version of the paragraph and producing a neat final copy. This is generally how paragraph writing should work.

WRITE: Develop a descriptive paragraph following the four steps in the writing process described below. (Use the space near the bottom of the page to begin your paragraph planning.)

1   Begin by *selecting* a subject for your descriptive paragraph. Make sure to pick a subject that interests you and will interest your reader. (Refer to "Topics, Sample" in the handbook index for possible writing ideas.)

2   Once you select a subject, *collect* information about it. Write a topic sentence (see the formula in your handbook), and gather ideas and details to support it in the body of your paragraph.

3   Now you're ready to write the first draft, to *connect* all of your thoughts. Begin with your topic sentence (unless you have a good reason not to), and follow with important facts and details. Have some idea as to how you want to arrange the details in your writing. Don't, however, be afraid to include interesting ideas that enter your mind as you write.

      Review your first draft, and revise those parts that need work.

4   Finally, *correct* any careless errors in the revised version of your description, and produce a "clean" final draft.

(after•words) Exchange finished products. Make note of the paragraph's *structure* as well as the paragraph's *ideas*.

■ Completing a Paragraph Frame

I've been framed!

(fore•words) A **writing frame** is a paragraph that is partly completed. It provides a writer with key words and phrases (framing words) that she or he can use as starting points for the sentences in the paragraph. Can a writer make changes in a writing frame? Yes, the frame is simply a guide. Changes can be made to meet the needs of each writer.

COMPLETE: Complete the following paragraph frame. Fill in the blank spaces with words and phrases that effectively complete each idea that is started for you. Make minor changes as necessary.

My father may be at a loss for words when he sees my closet, but I can describe it

perfectly. On the inside of the door, _____

_____ .

Hanging from the rod are not only _____

_____

but also _____ .

On the wooden shelf above the rod, _____

_____ .

Here I know I will always find _____

_____ .

On the floor, _____

_____ .

Finally, in the back, far from view, _____

_____ .

That's my closet from top to bottom!

(after•words) Share your completed frame. Then create paragraph frames of your own— and exchange them with your classmates. (Make these frames as serious or as crazy as you want.)

■ Methods of Arranging Details

Putting Things in Order

(fore•words) A florist creatively arranges flowers to make a beautiful bouquet. A graphic designer carefully arranges words and pictures to produce a powerful ad or poster. A writer deliberately arranges details to produce a meaningful and effective piece of writing.

IDENTIFY: Determine the methods of arrangement used in each of the following paragraphs. (Refer to "Methods . . ." in the handbook index for help.)

Example: _____ *chronological (time) order* _____

Last weekend was incredibly busy. On Friday evening we went out to dinner at the new restaurant on Washington Avenue. On Saturday we went horseback riding in the morning and swimming at Brown's Lake in the afternoon. Sunday we had a picnic at Johnson's Park. We hardly had time to squeeze in our homework that night.

1. _____

Our administration has recently adopted a closed-campus lunch hour. This means everyone has to brown-bag it or eat hot lunch—what a choice! Even those of us who live close to the school must stay on campus during the noon hour. There will be no more Friday lunches at Kewpees and no more walks around the block with friends, crunching into juicy apples. We can thank the careless behavior of a few students for this new restriction.

2. _____

My older brother Jack and his "wing nut" friend Joe Bombard have a lot in common. They both love cars. No, they live for cars. Heck, they're starting to look and smell like cars. They both are also devoted to pro wrestling. They could talk for hours about Hulk Hogan, Randy Savage, The Defender, and all of the rest of the "megawrestlers." Unfortunately, Jack and Joe are not so devoted to their schoolwork. They have trouble applying themselves in any of their classes—except for the shop classes. They even missed their final English exam, so now they must ask the school board for permission to take a special exam this summer. Before too long, either cars or pro wrestling will have to take a backseat to schoolwork. Otherwise, they'll find themselves in real trouble.

3. _____

The Special Olympics has taught us a great deal about the value of all human life. The mother of a little boy who is retarded described one Special Olympics event in a way I will always remember. She watched her son running that race, drawing closer and closer to the finish line. Only one other runner was close to the finish line, too, a short distance behind her son. Suddenly she heard the crowd groan as that child stumbled and took a nasty fall. Tensely, she watched her little boy turn back to help the fallen runner. Both hobbled across the finish line, arm in arm, to wild cheers from the crowd.

(after•words) Write a paragraph of your own modeled after one of the examples above.

■ Selecting and Using Details

Give me the facts.

REVIEW: Carefully read through the following list of facts about buffalo. Then select four (or more) related facts to develop into an effective paragraph. Make sure to add a topic sentence and a closing sentence. (Refer to the "Building Paragraphs" chapter in your handbook for helpful writing guidelines.)

FACTS SHEET ON BUFFALO

- recently reintroduced in the Badlands and Black Hills of South Dakota
- calves born from April through June
- belong to cattle family
- are also known as American bison
- generally live in bands of 50 to 200
- shaggy brown coats—sun-bleached gold on their humps
- shed coats in spring
- calves are yellowish red when born
- their "baby wool" replaced by shaggy coat by first fall
- originated in Asia
- two races: plains buffalo and the larger mountain buffalo
- most at home in prairie shortgrass country
- animals of the sun
- migrated here a million years ago
- eat buffalo grass and side-oats grama
- bulls fight for rights to a cow
- buffalo and pronghorn only hoofed mammals in North American prairie
- Nebraska once center of buffalo population
- head and horn scratching on pine trees stopped trees from spreading onto the prairie
- by June, the shedding of winter wool well along
- cows and calves live together until breeding season
- bulls join them for these seasons
- buffalo remain together through fall
- calves weigh 25 to 40 pounds at birth
- by fall of first year will weigh up to 400 pounds
- very old animals live alone
- bulls breed from 6 to 14 years of age
- cows may calve past 30 years of age
- bull larger than cow, stands nearly six feet at shoulders and weighs a ton
- cows reach half the weight of a bull
- from 1870's on hunters nearly wiped them out
- a few buffalo remained in Yellowstone region, descendants still found there today
- today no real predator, wolf once their "undertaker"
- by digging with hoofs, kept prairie primed for strong plants

(after•words) Exchange finished products. Make note of the paragraph's *structure* as well as the paragraph's *ideas*.

■ **Levels of Detail**

Controlling, Clarifying, Completing

(fore•words) Anyone who successfully plans a great party, produces a powerful video, or develops an award-winning science project pays special attention to detail. In this activity, you'll learn how paying special attention to detail can really make a difference in your writing.

READ & REACT: **In your handbook, carefully read about the three different levels of sentence detail.** (**Refer to "Paragraph, Detail" in the index.**) **Then, complete the following chart.**

❏ Level 1 details are contained in _____ sentences.

These sentences name _____ paragraph.

❏ Level 2 details are contained in _____ sentences.

These sentences contain details which make _____ reader.

❏ Level 3 details are contained in _____ sentences.

These sentences contain specific _____

_____ in Level 2 sentences.

LOCATE: **Here's a special challenge. Find sentences that contain the three different levels of detail in the first part of the model persuasive paragraph.** (**It's listed in the index under "Paragraph, Model paragraphs."**)

Level 1 Sentence: (Topic sentences are Level 1 sentences.) _____

_____

Level 2 Sentence: _____

_____

Level 3 Sentence: (There is more than one Level 3 sentence in the first part of this writing.)

_____

(after•words) In a persuasive paragraph, convince your readers that a certain person has three (or more) qualities that make him a true friend, a sworn enemy, a respected adult, etc. (Make sure to include all three levels of detail in your paragraph.)

WRITING A CHARACTER SKETCH

She led a "storied" life.

(fore•words) This unit is designed to help you write a brief, colorful **character sketch**. (A character sketch is a type of descriptive writing that provides a special look at a real person.) The key to writing an effective character sketch is selecting a good subject (*someone you know well*) and bringing that subject to life (*based on your knowledge of this person*).

COMPLETE: The main part of a character sketch is often a little story or anecdote that makes an important point about the subject. Complete the following open-ended sentences to help you think of possible subjects (and related anecdotes) for your sketch.

Example: The best time I ever had with _____ *Aunt Evie* _____ was

_____ *when we went to the beach in Ogunquit, Maine* _____ .

● I guess _____ was one of my all-time favorite teachers,

because _____ .

● When I hear the word "friend," _____ comes to mind immediately, because _____ .

● Of all the people I know, I'd most like to be like _____

because _____ .

● A day at school just wouldn't be the same without _____

because _____ .

● The most interesting person I've ever met is _____

because _____ .

● *(Your Choice)* _____

_____ .

(after•words) Put a check next to one of the sentences that you would like to use as a starting point for your character sketch. (Share your thoughts about your choice with a classmate.)

■ Model Character Sketch

READ: As you read the following model by student writer Anne Morrissy, notice how the sketch or description evolves around an anecdote:

Opposites Attract

The *topic sentence* is formed from one of the examples in the previous activity.

When I hear the word "friend," Karen immediately comes to mind. Karen has been my friend for as long as I can remember, even though we are opposites. If she says "black," I say "white." I'm a blond; she's a brunette. She's a risk-taker, and I'm not. Yet we've remained best friends since third grade.

An amusing anecdote supports the topic sentence.

I smile when I think of all of the ridiculous things we've done together. I recall the time we wanted to earn a cooking badge for girl scouts. We decided to teach cooking to the kids in our neighborhood, so we typed up fliers and stuffed them in mail boxes. Only two kids showed up, but we taught them everything we knew about cooking every day for a week. At the end, when we asked them what they had learned, the only thing they remembered was how to use a knife safely.

The writer ties all of her ideas together in the closing paragraph.

Still, I guess that's what a good friend is all about: a person who's willing to do dumb things with you and laugh about it later, a person with whom you have a lot of great memories. Karen and I are a pair, like peanut butter and jelly. We're great by ourselves, but together we're even better.

REACT: Carefully review the side notes to make sure you understand how the student writer developed her sketch. Then note in the space below what you like best about this model and what you might have done differently. (Share your responses.)

What you like best:	What you would have done differently:

HANDBOOK HELPER

Refer to "Character sketch" in the index for another model. Notice that this model revolves around one specific experience.

■ Collecting Details for Your Character Sketch

(fore•words) An effective character sketch considers the whole person, the person on the outside and on the inside. This means you should consider what physical *and* personal characteristics you want to emphasize in your writing.

IDENTIFY: List below any examples of physical or personal characteristics in the two model sketches.

HANDBOOK HELPER   Refer to "Character sketch" in the index if you're not sure what to look for in these models. The information listed under "Collecting: Gathering Details" in that section will help you.

"Opposites Attract"

● Physical: _____

● Personal: _____

Handbook Model (Untitled)

● Physical: _____

_____

● Personal: _____

_____

LIST: Now list one or two important physical and personal characteristics that your subject displays, especially when you think of the anecdote you would like to share about him or her.

Physical:

● _____

● _____

Personal:

● _____

● _____

■ Planning Your Sketch

COLLECTING: There are three important steps in planning your character sketch: (On your own paper, do some basic planning following these steps.)

1. **SELECT** one of the sentences from the sentence-completion activity as the opening idea in your writing. (You might have to work with this sentence until it says exactly what you want it to say.)

2. **DECIDE** which of your subject's physical or personal characteristics are important to emphasize. (There probably will be only one or two.)

3. **HAVE** an effective anecdote in mind about your subject to share with your readers. (This anecdote should reflect what is said about the subject in the opening sentence.)

Special Note: Once you have a feel for all of these working parts, you're ready to start writing.

WRITING THE FIRST DRAFT: Begin your first draft with one of the sentences (or a version of that sentence) from the first activity in this unit, and then work in any important physical or personal traits and your related anecdote.

EVALUATE: The following checklist will help you review and revise your first draft. (Use this same checklist to evaluate your classmates' work.)

____ **Organization:**   Does the character sketch begin with an effective opening sentence? Does the main part of the writing focus on a related anecdote?

____ **Detail:**   Has mention been made of any of the subject's physical or personal characteristics? Has the anecdote been presented in enough detail?

____ **Style:**   Can you tell by the writing how the writer really feels about the subject of the sketch?

____ **Mechanics:**   Has proper attention been given to neatness and accuracy? (Consider readability, sentences, spelling, punctuation, and grammar.)

■ Writing Prompt

We did everything together.

WRITE: Study the following writing prompt. Then write freely and rapidly for 5-10 minutes, focusing your thoughts and feelings on someone (perhaps a former friend) who was, at one time, a constant companion. (Have another piece of paper ready in case you run out of room.)

(after•words) Carefully review this writing, noting the words and ideas you especially like. Then continue writing and revising until you have produced an effective character sketch or sample of some other type of biographical writing.

■ **Writing Prompt**

Where (Who) are our heroes?

WRITE: Study the following writing prompt. Then write freely and rapidly for 5-10 minutes, focusing your thoughts and feelings on someone (perhaps a former friend) who was, at one time, a constant companion. (Have another piece of paper ready in case you run out of room.)

_____

_____

_____

_____

_____

_____

_____

_____

_____

_____

_____

_____

_____

_____

_____

_____

(after•words) Carefully review this writing, noting the words and ideas you especially like. Then continue writing and revising until you have produced an effective character sketch or sample of some other type of biographical writing.

WRITING MYTHS

It's all Greek to me . . .

(fore•words) Thousands of years ago, the Greeks, like all ancient people, found their world awesome . . . and confusing. What were those tremendous flashes of light in a stormy sky? Where did the ball of blazing brightness come from each morning? What caused the sunny blue skies of summer to turn cold and gray in the wintertime? Why were there so many varieties of plants and animals? What? Where? Why?

In an effort to understand their world, the Greeks created stories to explain the wonders of nature. In many of these stories, amazing supermen (gods) and superwomen (goddesses) with unusual powers were responsible for the normal and not so normal occurrences in life. As you know, these special stories are called **myths**. In this unit, you will become apprentice mythmakers, learning about and writing original myths.

LIST: **What questions about life might you have asked had you been living in ancient Greece? (List at least four.)**

Example: *Why do some trees lose their leaves?*

1. _____

_____

2. _____

_____

3. _____

_____

4. _____

_____

5. _____

_____

(after•words) Put a check next to one of these questions that you would like to explore and explain in a myth.

■ **Understanding Myths**

The Role of the Gods

(fore•words) Gods and goddesses are key elements/characters in most myths, especially in the ancient Greek and Roman cultures. It is through the actions of these super beings that many of the mysteries of the natural world and human nature are explained.

Simple Greek Myth

Phaethon, son of Apollo (the sun god), was so stubborn and foolish that he ignored his father's advice and drove the golden chariot (the sun) wildly and lost control of it over northern Africa. Phaethon's chariot came down dangerously close to the earth and burned the land known today as the Sahara Desert. To protect the rest of the earth, the king of the gods, Zeus, zapped Phaethon with a mighty thunderbolt and killed him.

Discussion: The ancient Greeks really believed their myths and held them sacred. They also believed that someone who ignored a father's advice, or remained foolishly stubborn like Phaethon, might cause her or his own destruction.

IDENTIFY: List two or three other qualities of human nature, like *stubbornness* or *carelessness,* that might prove as difficult to explain as the wonders of nature.

Creature Features

Storytellers quickly learned that if people enjoyed hearing about a two-headed snake, they'd love hearing about a giant, fifty-headed, poisonous snake (Hydra) that sprouted two more heads each time one was cut off by a superhero (Hercules).

CREATE: Give each of the following animals or individuals a special power, a power that really makes each one a mythical character. (Share your results.)

a bird (of prey) _____

a young goddess _____

an old messenger _____

(Your choice) _____

■ Original Myth 1

READ: This myth attempts to explain how chocolate, once the food of the gods, must now be eaten with care, especially by anyone trying to watch his or her weight. (It was written by a calorie-counting middle-school teacher.)

Ambrosia's Anger

On Mount Olympus, the gods loved the sight of Ambrosia. Her cocoa-colored hair, bittersweet chocolate-brown eyes, and gown of flowing silk the shade of milk chocolate made her a vision of beauty. Around her neck, the goddess of chocolate wore a necklace of Hershey Kiss-shaped stones, each one bearing a letter of her name. Her five-foot scepter had been carved from the wood of her most-prized cocoa tree and topped with a glowing crystal. How she loved treating the gods and goddesses to her chocolate ambrosia, the sweetest of all the refreshments on Mount Olympus.

Unfortunately the beautiful goddess sometimes spent more time being admired for her loveliness than attending to her cocoa plants. So, one summer day as Ambrosia strolled through her lush cocoa plantations on the east slopes of Mount Olympus, she noticed a dreaded little beast plucking her precious cocoa beans. Suddenly the creature reared its ugly head, stopped cramming beans into its kangaroo-ish pouch, and fled. (With one destructive touch, it doomed any food to be disastrously high in calories—forever. Sadly, no mortal or immortal had ever outwitted the hated Caloric Creature.) Incensed, Ambrosia chased the beast from her fields. And then swinging her mighty scepter, she banished the beast from her plantation, but not before the Caloric Creature, as he came to be known, had cursed every cocoa tree with only high-calorie beans.

In her fury, Ambrosia uprooted all of her beloved chocolate trees and transplanted them in faraway Brazil. Because she could not undo the damage done by the Caloric Creature, Ambrosia wept bitterly at the fate of her favorite food. Now mortals and immortals alike would be doomed to count their calories whenever they wished to enjoy the food of the gods and goddesses—Ambrosia's beloved chocolate.

(after•words) As you can see, this myth is styled and structured much like a traditional Greek myth. Myths from other cultures—Norse, Hindu, African, Native American—may be styled and structured in different ways, in ways that might be more to your own liking when it comes to writing an original myth.

■ Analyzing a Myth

COMPLETE: Identify the basic story elements of "Ambrosia's Anger" by completing the following chart. (Work on this activity with a classmate if your teacher allows it.)

•   **CHARACTERS:** *(Who is involved in this myth?)*

•   **SETTING:** *(Where does it take place?)*

•   **PLOT:** *(List three or four important things that happened.)*

•   **STYLE:** *(List three or four phrases or ideas that make "Ambrosia's Anger" sound or read like a myth. Example: "the gods loved the sight of Ambrosia")*

Special Challenge: To see if "Ambrosia's Anger" does, in fact, contain some of the essential qualities of a Greek myth, complete the following chart.

1. Note one or two references to nature.	2. List any Greek gods or goddesses mentioned in the myth.
3. Describe any special creature in the myth.	4. Identify one example of an other-worldly (or super) action.
5. Cite one comment, made directly or indirectly, about human nature.	

(after•words) Discuss the results of your work as a class. (It's important that everyone understands the working parts of a myth.)

■ Original Myth 2

READ: The following myth was written by Hillary Bachman when she was an eighth-grade student. (The title identifies what this myth attempts to explain.)

Why Sea Turtles Cry

Long ago on the Aegean coast, there lived a beautiful goddess named Turtalina. Goddess of the sand, Turtalina ruled over everything living in and on the special ground between the water and the land. No one could build anything there.

One day Turtalina was feeding the seagulls when a handsome man came by. Normally, she would have run away from him because mortals were not to see such beautiful women. Instead, she stayed and he came up to her. He was stunned by her beauty and asked her to take a walk. Although she knew that she was never to leave the beach, she followed him.

They were gone for days, and because there was no one to take care of the creatures on the beach, all turned to chaos. Now Poseidon, god of the sea, knew something was wrong when he heard the seagulls fighting for food. He looked out of the sea one day and saw that Turtalina and the man had returned and built a house on the sand.

Before this time, the sea was still. There were no waves. But Poseidon grew angry with Turtalina's actions and blew the water until it came crashing down on her house. She and the man were swept out to sea. The man died, but Turtalina was allowed to live. Poseidon decided from then on that no one would be in charge of the sand, that everything would have to take care of itself. He continued to blow water into waves to destroy any structure on the beach. But saddest of all, he turned Turtalina into a creature of the sea, a sea turtle, who would be ugly and clumsy on land.

The only time she could go to the beach was to lay her eggs in the sand. Every time she returned to the sand, she started to cry because she remembered the man she loved and how she used to rule the beach. But most of all she cried because she could never see her babies or take care of them. They had to survive on their own when they hatched.

(after•words) Analyze this myth by identifying the basic story elements and by noting its mythic qualities—much like you did for "Ambrosia's Anger." (Work on this analysis with a classmate.)

■ Creating Story Ideas for a Myth

PLAN: Now that you have read and analyzed three myths (this includes the story of Phaethon), you should be ready to plan your own myth. Use the following checklist as a planning guide.

_____ **BASE** your myth on something that is naturally occurring. (Look at your work in the first activity for ideas.)

_____ **SELECT** a main character (or characters) for your myth. (This main character does not have to be a god or goddess. Many stories are based on the relationship a mortal human being has with a god or goddess.)

_____ **DECIDE** if your main character is going to have any special qualities, and if she or he will display a particular personality trait (stubbornness, bravery, pity, etc.).

_____ Also, **CONSIDER** including a creature or monster in your myth. (Myths are often a struggle between good and evil, between the good main character and the evil creature or monster. But also know that a creature is not an essential element in a myth.)

_____ **IDENTIFY** where your story will take place. (The setting does not have to be anything really special. The action could simply take place in an ordinary woods.)

_____ **DETERMINE** what will happen first . . . and maybe second in your myth. (It would be hard to know any more than that until you start writing.)

(after•words) Don't worry if you can't make all of these choices _before_ you start writing. Many of the important decisions about your myth can be made _while_ you write.

■ **Writing and Revising Your Myth**

Writing the First Draft

WRITE: Develop your first draft freely and openly, using any planning you may have done as a basic guide. (Refer to the model if you need help with your writing.)

Special Note: All stories, including myths, are based on the following simple framework: *There is a main character (or creature) in a place doing some activity, and a conflict or problem occurs.* So get your main character involved in some activity and go from there.

EVALUATE: The following checklist will help you review and revise your first draft. (Use this same checklist to evaluate your classmates' work.)

_____ **Organization:** Is the myth based on a series of related events (the plot) that builds in interest throughout the story?

_____ **Detail:** Are the characters and their actions described effectively?

_____ **Style:** Does the story read like a myth? Does it include a god, a goddess, or an unusual creature? Does it contain any supernatural occurrences and/or superhuman actions? Does it have anything to say about human nature?

_____ **Mechanics:** Has proper attention been given to neatness and accuracy? (Consider spelling, punctuation and grammar.)

(Additional comments when reviewing a classmate's work)

_____ What do you like best about this myth?

_____ What changes would you recommend?

(after•words) Share your finished product with your classmates. Then write additional Greek myths or myths based on different cultures.

■ **Writing an Original Myth**

Back to the Future

extended
ACTIVITY

    People created myths to explain things that puzzled them, especially natural things like snow or floods. They even tried to explain aspects of human nature like laziness or courage.

CREATE: Write a myth, as if you were an ancient Greek, explaining a cellular phone, a video camera, freeze-dried food, or some other modern invention to the people living in those ancient times. (Use the space below for planning and your first draft.)

(after•words) Share your results out loud. Read your myth with feeling, as if you have an incredible story to tell.

WRITING ABOUT PROBLEMS AND SOLUTIONS

You think you've got problems!

(fore•words) Have you ever had to solve a problem? Did you leave your homework at school? Have you ever run out of money just when you need to buy a family member a present? Have you ever tried to convince your parents to let you attend a concert? Real-life problems need solutions.

Solving a problem is a step-by-step process. Along the way you must identify the problem (that's usually the easy part), describe its effect on you or others, think about possible solutions, choose the best solution, and so on.

In this unit, you will learn a valuable problem-solving strategy and explore different types of problems (personal, environmental, community-related, etc.). One positive result of thinking and writing about problems is it teaches you how to write clearly and logically, and that's something that will help you in ALL of your writing assignments!

CLASSIFY: For each category, list at least three problems. (An example is provided under each category.)

Personal
(My parents won't let me go to concerts.)

Community
(There's nothing for teenagers to do.)

Environmental
(There is so much waste at fast-food restaurants.)

Health/Medical
(Hospital patients are not treated with respect or dignity.)

(after•words) Share your "problems" with a classmate. Then choose one problem that you would be interested in exploring further.

■ Problem-Solving Strategy: The IDEAL Solution

Discovering the Ideal Solution

APPLY: Use the IDEAL Solution strategy to solve one of the personal problems you listed in the previous activity. (Example responses are provided in parentheses.)

Problem-Solving Strategy: The **IDEAL** Solution

State your goal: (*I want my parents to let me go to the L. L. Cool J concert.*)

_____

1. **I**dentify the problem: (*My parents say I'm too young to go to concerts.*)

_____

2. **D**escribe the problem: (*If I pay for the ticket, I should be allowed to go.*)

_____

_____

3. **E**xplore possible solutions: (*I could earn the right to go by working extra hard at home and at school. I could ask an older sister to go with me. I could have someone I know talk to my parents about concerts.*)

_____

_____

_____

4. **A**ct: [Write out your best solutions.] (*My older sister could go with me.*) _____

_____

5. **L**ook at the effects or results: (*Even though I really want to go just with my friends, I would still get to the concert. Besides, once my parents find out that I know how to act, they might let me go to future concerts "unattended."*)

_____

_____

(after•words) Turn your **IDEAL** solution into a short problem-solving paragraph, working in the ideas as you have them listed above. (Share your results.)

■ Problem-Solving Strategy: The IDEAL Solution

Proposing and Persuading

(fore•words) Many students in your class are concerned about the environment. They believe it's important for everyone to help protect the earth. One of your classmates feels that either people aren't aware of environmental problems or they don't think the problems are serious. *So you and your classmates decide to make other people more aware of the needs of our environment. How will you do this?*

APPLY: Create a course of action using the IDEAL Solution framework below. (Work on this activity with a classmate if your teacher allows it. And make sure to share your results.)

Problem-Solving Strategy: The **IDEAL** Solution

State your goal: _____

1. **I**dentify the problem: _____

2. **D**escribe the problem: _____

   _____

   _____

3. **E**xplore possible solutions or actions: _____

   _____

   _____

   _____

4. **A**ct: [Write out your best solutions/plans and then select one master plan.]

   _____

   _____

   _____

5. **L**ook at the effects or results: _____

   _____

Special Challenge: Put one of your ideas into practice! Design a poster or compose a Public Service Announcement (PSA) for a radio or TV station.

■ Writing a Problem/Solution Paragraph

(fore•words) Many neighborhoods and communities face serious problems. Some are easily solved: *A car wash may pay for new sports equipment for a local youth center.* Some problems are more challenging: *How, for example, could little children feel safer in a playground that is also a hangout for local teenagers?*

READ: Read the following problem/solution model paragraph.

Graffiti is a big problem in our neighborhood. Local teenagers spray-paint slogans, symbols, and pictures all over the buildings and sidewalks. It's embarrassing when someone comes to your house and there's graffiti all over the outside. I think that one of the reasons why teenagers write graffiti is because they don't feel like they belong. Writing graffiti is one way of putting their signature on something. I think we could solve this problem by inviting local teenagers to paint murals on certain buildings. First, they would have to help paint the buildings where there is graffiti. Then, they could plan and paint murals that expressed their feelings and their hopes for the neighborhood. Once they feel proud of what they've done, they won't want it ruined by graffiti. And they won't paint over anyone else's either because they know their mural will be next. I know that this solution has worked in other neighborhoods, and I think it would work in my neighborhood, too!

Discussion: Note that the topic sentence of this paragraph identifies the basic problem (*"Graffiti is a big problem . . ."*). In the body of the paragraph, the problem is explained, plus a workable solution is offered and analyzed.

➤ *Now You Try*

SELECTING & COLLECTING: Choose a community or neighborhood problem to explore in a problem/solution paragraph. Then apply the IDEAL Solution strategy to help you organize your thoughts about your problem. (Do this work on your own paper.)

WRITE: Complete the first draft of your paper working in ideas as you have them listed in your planning. (Refer to the model paragraph above for help.)

■ Reviewing and Revising Your Paragraph

EVALUATE: The following checklist will help you review and revise your work. (Use the same checklist to evaluate your classmates' work.)

_____ **Organization:** Does the paragraph begin with a clearly stated problem (the topic sentence)? Are the supporting ideas logical and arranged in the best possible order?

_____ **Detail:** Do all of the details in the paragraph describe the problem?

_____ **Style:** Does the paragraph read smoothly and clearly from start to finish? Has a solution to the problem been presented in the best possible way?

_____ **Mechanics:** Has proper attention been given to neatness and accuracy? (Look for complete sentences, spelling errors, and proper punctuation and grammar.)

Special Group Challenge

As you know, writing convincing problem/solution papers requires clear and logical thinking. You can't be fuzzy or unclear, or take shortcuts in your thinking.

ANALYZE: Working with a classmate, decide which type of misleading or fuzzy thinking shows up in each one of these sentences. (Use the handbook to complete this work.)

HANDBOOK HELPER Refer to "Thinking, Logically" in the index. Once you turn to that section, look for "Avoid Fuzzy Thinking."

Example: Don't worry about wearing a bicycle helmet—millions of bicyclists don't.

   Only supported by the fact that many people feel this way. _____

● We've had rain two days in a row. Looks like the drought is finally going to end.

   _____

● The judge should give the criminal a break because that's the American way.

   _____

● Brown's Grocery is a crummy store because it closes every night at 6:00.

   _____

● (Write your own fuzzy statement.) _____

   _____

■ Problem-Solving Strategy: MAPPING

Mapping the Problem

extended **ACTIVITY**

Sometimes it helps to "map out" a problem to help you solve it. Carefully review the following explanation of a problem-solving mapping strategy.

A. THE PROBLEM
- Write the specific problem in the center of the map.
- List one or two reasons for the problem.

B. SOME POSSIBLE SOLUTIONS
- List two or three possible solutions.
- Put a * next to the best solution.

C. THE RESULTS
- List two or three changes (or results) that may occur because of your best solution.

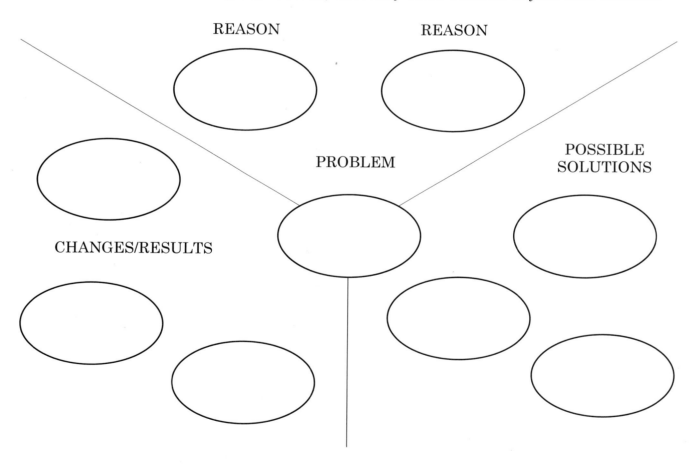

COMPLETE: Map out a problem related to school by filling in the map above or by creating a new one on your own paper. Then write a problem/solution paper working in the ideas as listed in your map. (Refer to the explanation at the top of this page for help with this problem-solving strategy.)

■ Writing a Problem-Solution Essay

(fore•words) Up to this point, you've been asked to develop problem/solution paragraphs. In this section of the unit, you'll learn about and apply a strategy for exploring a problem in a multiparagraph essay.

REVIEW: Carefully review the steps in this strategy.

TWO-PART STRATEGY

- **Begin** with a starter sentence about your subject once you have done some thinking and talking about it. Your starter sentence will look like this: (You fill in the problem and the solution.)

      ____*This problem*____ has resulted in ____*this situation or solution*____ .

                                      or

      ____*This problem*____ has caused us to ____*get involved in this situation*____ .

- **Explore** the first part of your starter sentence—the problem—in a 5-10 minute free writing. (Review this free writing, and share it with classmates.)

- Then **explore** the second part of your starter sentence—the situation or solution—in another 5-10 minute free writing. (Review and share this writing as well.)

- **Develop** an opening paragraph for your essay. (Your opening paragraph should include your starter sentence plus a few additional sentences which add introductory detail.)

- After the opening paragraph is set, **write** the main part of your essay using the information in each of your free writings as the starting point for your work. (You will need to develop at least two paragraphs here—one discussing the problem and another one discussing the resulting situation.)

   Continue to work on your essay until it says what you want it to say.

(after•words) Notice that the key to this strategy is developing an effective starter sentence. This sentence controls the rest of the essay.

■ Writing Starter Sentences

WRITE: Think of a problem (personal, community-related, global) that you would like to explore in your essay following this two-part strategy. Then write a starter sentence for your work. *Remember:* The first part of this sentence states the problem and the second part identifies the resulting situation. (Use the space below to write your sentence. Expect to write two or three versions before you get it just right.)

Examples:

Suppose someone close to you has become too demanding of your time. A possible starter sentence could be as follows:

Lee's constant need for my attention has resulted _in a strain in our relationship_ .
　　　　　(the problem)　　　　　　　　　　　　　(the situation)

Or suppose you and your friends have a hard time finding things to do for recreation. A possible starter sentence may be as follows:

The closing of the Youth Center has _hurt our neighborhood_ .
　　　　(the problem)　　　　　　　　　(the situation)

Final Version: _____

■ Exploring the Problem

WRITE FREELY: Use the space below to write freely for 5 to 10 minutes about the problem identified in the first part of your starter sentence. (In the example starter sentences, "Lee's constant need for my attention" and "The closing of the Youth Center" are the problems.)

(after•words) Review your free writing, noting ideas you especially like as well as things you might want to add. (Share your work with a classmate.)

■ Exploring the Resulting Situation

WRITE FREELY: Use the space below to write freely for 5 to 10 minutes about the resulting situation identified in the second part of your starter sentence. (In the example starter sentences, "a strain in our relationship" and "hurt our neighborhood" are the resulting situations.)

_____

_____

_____

_____

_____

_____

_____

_____

_____

_____

_____

_____

_____

_____

_____

_____

(after•words) Review your free writing, noting ideas you especially like as well as things you might want to add. (Share your work with a classmate.)

■ Writing an Opening Paragraph

WRITE: Develop an opening paragraph for your essay that includes your starter sentence plus a few introductory sentences. (Use the space provided below to work on this paragraph. Don't be surprised if you have to write two or three versions of this paragraph before you get it "right.")

Example Opening Paragraph:

> I've never thought of myself as a private person. I enjoy the company of my mom and older brother. I have a great time with my friends Missy and Sharla. We have so much fun talking and laughing and acting silly. I never feel crowded with any of these people. We just seem to know when enough is enough. I can't say the same for my boyfriend Lee. *His constant need for attention has resulted in a strain in our relationship.*

Introductory Details

Starter Sentence

Your Opening Paragraph:

(after•words) In the example above, the writer establishes her relationship with other important people in her life, and then turns her attention to Lee, the subject of her essay. Review your own paragraph to make sure that the first few sentences effectively lead into your subject.

■ Developing the Main Part of Your Essay

(fore•words) Once you have an opening paragraph in place, next turn your attention to the main part or body of the essay. It is in this part of your work that you will again address the two main parts in your starter sentence (just as you did in your free writings). Your work at this step in the process may consist of a basic tightening up (cutting, rewording, etc.) of both free writings, or, now that you have completed your opening paragraph, you may have thought of new ideas to add.

WRITE: Whatever the case may be, it is now time to develop the ideas that support your starter sentence. Write at least one paragraph supporting the first part of the starter sentence—the problem. (Base this paragraph on the main ideas in your first free writing.) And write at least one paragraph supporting the second part of your starter sentence—the resulting situation. (Base this paragraph on your second free writing). Use the space below to start on your work.

(after•words) As with any piece of writing, it's almost impossible to get everything right the first time. So be prepared to do some rewriting.

■ Completing Your Essay

(fore•words) Up to this point, you have developed the opening and supporting paragraphs of your essay. The most effective way to bring your work to a close is to explore a workable solution (or two) to your problem. This will help you come full circle with your essay.

WRITE: Use the space below to work on a closing paragraph that explores a workable solution to your problem. (Don't, however, force this paragraph. If your essay seems to end naturally and effectively without another paragraph tacked on, that's fine.)

EVALUATE: The following checklist will help you review and revise your essay. (Use the same checklist to evaluate your classmates' work.)

_____ **Organization:** Is the writing organized around a problem clearly stated in a starter sentence?

_____ **Detail:** Is each part of the essay developed in enough detail?

_____ **Style:** Does the writing include an effective opening and closing paragraph? Does the essay read honestly and naturally?

_____ **Mechanics:** Has proper attention been given to neatness and accuracy?

WRITING A REPORT

If I were a carpenter or a dentist . . .

(fore•words) In this unit you will learn all about report writing—from selecting an interesting subject to collecting facts and details, from organizing all of your information to writing and revising a first draft. The skills and strategies that you practice here will help you write reports in all of your classes, now and in the future. Your work in this unit will also have an important real-world application, since you will be asked to report on a specific career or job that interests you.

Special Note: Your handbook contains guidelines and examples that will help you at each step in the report-writing process. (Refer to "Report, The Classroom" in the index for this information.)

COMPLETE: There are thousands and thousands of different careers in the world of work. Which one you choose for your report depends upon your background and interests. To get started, complete the chart below, using the "Essentials of Life Checklist" in the handbook as your guide. (Refer to the index for this information.) Fill in the first column of this chart with different essentials of life. Then list three or four different careers related to each of these categories. (Two of the lines have been filled in for you.)

Essentials of Life	Related Careers
clothing	*fashion designer, model, clothing-store manager*
exercise	*team trainer, physical therapist, health-club operator*

(after•words) Review your list and put a check mark next to any careers that really interest you. Then share your work with two or three of your classmates to see what careers they listed.

■ **Selecting a Subject**

Surveying the Field

LIST: Complete the following survey to identify additional careers to consider for your report. List at least two or three careers after each question. (The careers listed in the chart on the next page will give you a few ideas for your survey. Also, your teacher or librarian may be able to give you some resources that list different types of careers.)

Which careers seem best suited to your interests, skills, and talents? _____

_____

_____

Which careers seem very exciting to you? _____

_____

_____

Which careers listed in the chart (or elsewhere) are totally new to you?

_____

_____

Which careers will probably become more and more important in the future?

_____

_____

What unusual, specialized, or old occupations interest you? (Blacksmithing would be an

example.) _____

_____

What do your parents, relatives, or neighbors do for a living? _____

_____

_____

_____

CAREER IDEAS

Accountant
Actor
Air Traffic Controller
Architect
Astronomer
Banker
Bookbinder
Buyer
Carpenter
Chemist
Childcare Worker
Computer Programmer
Construction Worker
Cosmetologist
Counselor
Dentist
Designer
Dietician
Doctor
Editor
Electrician

Engineer
Farmer
Firefighter
Forester
Graphic Designer
Hotel Manager
Keypunch Operator
Lawyer
Librarian
Machinist
Mechanic
Nurse
Optometrist
Pharmacist
Photographer
Plumber
Police Officer
Psychologist

Public Relations Worker
Radio/TV Personality or
    Technician
Receptionist
Reporter
Roofer
Social Worker
Speech Therapist
Surveyor
Teacher
Truck Driver
Upholsterer
Veterinarian
Welder
Woodworker

REVIEW: **Put a check next to two or three careers in your survey that you would really like to investigate for a report. Share your ideas with your classmates. You should also share your career ideas with one of your parents or another adult.**

Special Challenge: Write freely for 5 or 10 minutes about the careers or jobs held by some of your family members, relatives, or neighbors. Include any personal experiences you may have had related to their work.

(after•words) Review the different careers you have checked or written about during the opening activities in this unit. Then decide on one career as the subject for your report. List your subject on this line:

_____

■ **Setting the Scene for Research**

What do you know?

(fore•words) Once you've decided upon a career for your report, the next step is to figure out what you know about it, and what you still need to find out.

COMPLETE: To help you begin your research, fill in the following chart. List as many ideas as you can. (Make sure to share your work with a classmate.)

Career Subject: _____

List what you already know.   List what you would like to find out
                                     (in the form of questions).

_____   _____

_____   _____

_____   _____

_____   _____

_____   _____

_____   _____

_____   _____

_____   _____

REVIEW: Carefully review your work. Some of the ideas in your first list may help you when you write your first draft. (For example, you could introduce your report by describing some of the things you already know about your subject.)

The ideas in your second list will be more important at this point because they will help you collect information about your subject. Order these ideas by placing a 1 next to the most important one, a 2 next to the second most important idea, and so on. Finding information related to the ideas with high ratings (1, 2, and 3) should be given first priority.

■ Setting the Scene for Research

A-clustering we will go.

extended **ACTIVITY**

EXPLORE: Another way to gather your first thoughts about your subject is to cluster ideas around it. You can find specific guidelines and a model cluster in the handbook. (Refer to "Clustering" in the index.)

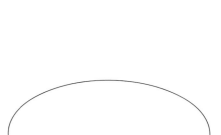

(Career)

Special Note: After you cluster for 3 or 4 minutes, a dominant idea about the subject usually comes to mind. More thoughts will come to mind by exploring this dominant idea in a nonstop free writing (5 minutes).

(after•words) Carefully review your clustering (and writing), paying special attention to the questions and ideas related to your career that you would like to investigate. Put a star next to each one of these ideas. Then share your work with your classmates.

■ Finding Sources of Information

Resources for Research

(fore•words) A report is only as good as the information it contains, so it is important to find as many facts and details as you possibly can from different types of resources (reference books, magazines, interviews, etc.). It is also important that you consult current resources to ensure that your facts are up-to-date as well as informative.

IDENTIFY: Listed on the next two pages are the most common categories of resources available to you for research. For each category (or as many as possible), locate and record titles of publications and names of individuals that might prove helpful during your research. You may have to consult the card catalog, the *Readers' Guide to Periodical Literature*, and the vertical file in your library to find books, magazines, and pamphlets. (Refer to "Library" in the handbook index for guidelines.)

Special Note: Record enough information about each resource so you can find it later on. If you are expected to include a bibliography with your report, you may want to list your resources according to the guidelines in the handbook. (Refer to "Bibliography" in the index for this information.)

Resources Planning Sheet

Person in this field:

_____

_____

Teacher or counselor:

_____

_____

Other individuals:

_____

_____

Reference books:

_____

_____

Other books:

_____

_____

_____

Magazines:

_____

_____

_____

Newspapers:

_____

_____

Pamphlets and booklets:

_____

_____

Places to visit:

_____

_____

_____

Other (videos, filmstrips, etc.):

_____

_____

(after•words) You won't have the time, the ability, or the need to consult all of these sources of information. Instead, you should select the ones that seem the most valuable (and accessible) and begin your research. Also remember that your teacher may require you to consult a certain number of resources.

■ Interviewing an Expert

May I ask you a few questions?

(fore•words) One of the most valuable sources of information available to you is other people. And the best way to get valuable information from other people is to interview them. You can learn all about the interviewing process in the handbook. (Refer to "Interviewing" in the index.)

    The following worksheet will help you prepare for any interviews for your career report.

Career Interview Worksheet

Person's name:

Place of business:

Job title:

Date, time, and location of interview:

Phone number:

1. How would you describe your job?

2. What are your important job responsibilities?

3. What do you like most about your job?

4. What is the most difficult part of your work?

    (List other questions that you would like to ask about a particular career.)

5.

6.

7.

(after•words) Interview someone you know about his or her career (a parent, a neighbor, etc.) before you conduct an official interview for your report.

■ **Collecting Information**

Using Note Cards

(fore•words) You are now ready to begin collecting information about your career. To organize your collecting, follow the basic plan as described and illustrated on this page.

WRITE: Record each of your questions from the "What do you know?" exercise on the top of a separate note card or half sheet of paper. (Skip any questions that do not seem really important. Also add questions if needed.) Then, each time you find a fact that helps answer one of your questions, write this information on the note card with that question.

Sample Note Cards

What training is needed to become a programmer?

What is the future outlook for this field?

What does a computer programmer do?
- talks with people to find out what they need in a program
- writes programs for operating computers, robots, and other computerized machinery
- writes instructions in computer language for every step in a certain task
- finds errors or glitches in programs

(Refer to "Report, Sample note cards" in the handbook index for more examples.)

RECORDING INFORMATION: When you list information on a note card, write clearly and neatly, using your own words as much as possible. Write phrases that highlight the main ideas rather than complete sentences. If you want to quote someone directly, make sure to get this person's exact words on paper; also list the person's name, the page number of the quote, and the title of the book it came from. (The names and page numbers will come in handy later if you need to give credit for information in your report.)

■ Organizing Your Information

Arranging Your Notes

(fore•words) Once you have collected all of your information, your next step is to organize your ideas for writing. Choose the information on one of your note cards to be the main idea of your report. For example, the main idea of a report on computer programming might be "Opportunities for computer programmers are excellent."

WRITE & ARRANGE: In the space provided below, express the main idea of your report in a clear sentence. (The main idea should focus on an important part of the career or on an overall feeling you have about it.)

Main Idea: _____

_____

_____

Then arrange the rest of your note cards in the best possible order. Keep the main point of your report in mind as you order your note cards.

OUTLINE: Next, on your own paper, organize your notes into a *rough outline*. Simply list the headings (questions) that are written at the top of your note cards in the order that you have just arranged them. Leave enough space after each heading to list the important facts or details from each note card. Follow this format:

Career: _____

Question: _____
    — *(important facts and details)*
    —
    —
    —

Question: _____
    —
    —
    —

(after•words) If you are expected to complete a more formal outline, rewrite your first version into a clear *sentence outline*. For example, a question like "What does a programmer do?" should be rewritten as a statement like "A programmer has many different responsibilities." (Refer to "Report, Sample outline" in the index for specific guidelines for using Roman numerals—I., II., III., etc.—and capital letters.)

■ **Connecting: Writing the First Draft**

Putting Your Ideas Together

(fore•words) If you have completed an outline, writing the *body* of your report should not be difficult. Basically, each main point (or question) in your outline becomes the topic sentence of a paragraph. The details under each main point become supporting sentences. However, writing the opening and closing paragraphs requires a little extra attention.

The Opening Paragraph

The beginning paragraph in your report should say something catchy, surprising, or important to hook your readers' interest. Search through all of your selecting and collecting notes for opening ideas. Perhaps you have an interesting personal story about this career to share. After the first few sentences, introduce the main idea of your report.

Special Note: For an example, read the opening paragraph for the model report in the handbook. (Refer to "Report, Model report" in the index.)

WRITE: Use the space provided here (or use your own paper) to plan and write your opening paragraph. Make sure to ask at least one of your classmates to react to your ideas. Once you feel satisfied with your opening, you may continue writing the rest of your report.

_____

_____

_____

_____

_____

_____

The Closing Paragraph

The final paragraph should summarize the main points in your report and leave readers with a lasting thought or impression about your career. (If, however, your report seems to come to a natural and effective ending after you've made the last point, a closing paragraph may not be necessary.)

(after•words) Always keep your readers in mind when you write your first draft. Don't tell them things that they already know. Instead, give them what's new, what's different, and what's important.

■ Reviewing and Revising Your First Draft

Refining Your Writing

EVALUATE: The following checklist will help you review and revise the first draft of your report. (Use this same checklist to evaluate your classmates' work.)

_____ **Organization:** Are all of the paragraphs organized in an effective way? Is the main point of each paragraph clear? Are all of the supporting ideas and details arranged in a logical order?

_____ **Detail:** Are enough details provided to give readers a clear understanding of this career?

_____ **Style:** Does the report contain effective opening and closing paragraphs? Is there a main idea or specific part of the career that is emphasized? Has there been an attempt to inform and entertain the readers?

_____ **Mechanics:** Has proper attention been given to neatness and accuracy? (Look for complete sentences, correct spelling, and proper punctuation and grammar.)

Special Note: Always follow your teacher's guidelines for writing the final copy of your report. She or he may have specific requirements concerning the type of paper you use, margins, page numbering, and so on.

Adding a Bibliography, a Title Page, and an Outline

If you are required to include a bibliography (works cited page), a title page, and an outline with your report, see your handbook for guidelines. (Refer to "Report, Bibliography" in the index for this information.)

Adding Other Elements

You might want to add charts, graphs, photographs, or illustrations to your report. If that is the case, make sure that you present this information as clearly, neatly, and accurately as you can.

(after•words) Share your finished report with your classmates, perhaps as part of a special career day. If an interview played an important role in your report, make sure that the person you spoke with receives a copy of your work.

PART II
Writing Workshops

PREWRITING STRATEGIES

Selecting and Collecting Ideas

(fore•words) Writing should be "fun," especially when you first put pen or pencil to paper. Don't be surprised by this. When you first start out, you don't have to worry about the look or the sound of your writing. This is the time to collect ideas, to search and shape your thinking, to stretch your imagination. The end result of your collecting can be very exciting. If you let yourself go and explore freely, you're bound to hit upon any number of new and exciting ideas that will set in motion a satisfying writing experience.

So how do you "let yourself go" in writing? You try the things we have provided for you in the following **Prewriting Strategies**. That includes, among other things, free writing, listing, "co-listing," and clustering.

Special Note: We call these strategies because they are tried and tested methods of discovery you will want to use again and again. (Refer to "Selecting" and "Collecting" in your handbook index for more information.)

User's Checklist

Check your progress as you work on these **Prewriting Strategies.**

- [ ] **Free Writing** • *It was only a joke!*

- [ ] **Clustering** • *"And now, a few words from our sponsor . . ."*

- [ ] **Listing** • *Now, how do I get out of this one?*

- [ ] **Cooperative Listing** • *Wheel of Foolishness*

- [ ] **Brainstorming** • *Solving Problems*

- [ ] **Story Frames** • *The Temple of Gloom*

- [ ] **Story Starters** • *Suddenly . . . !*

- [ ] **Imaginary Conversation** • *Thanks for the tip!*

- [ ] **Scrap Writing** • *Toss it!*

- [ ] **Observing and Recording** • *A Walking Tour*

(after • words) Prewriting is perhaps the most important step in the writing process. Some experts say that at least one-third of a writer's time should be devoted to this exploratory stage of writing. Keep that in mind when you start your next composition. Start out with a cluster or a co-list or a . . .

FREE WRITING

PREWRITING STRATEGY

Free writing *is one of the best forms of prewriting, especially for personal writing topics. When you free-write, you simply open up your mind and let the thoughts pour out—freely. Once you start, you should not stop writing until all your thoughts on the topic are down on paper.*

It was only a joke!

We've all played practical jokes on our friends and families (and they've played them on us). A good practical joke is one which truly fools the victim and gets them to do something that afterward seems very silly. A good practical joke is also one that's safe and doesn't put anyone in physical danger. What is the best practical joke you've ever pulled (or heard about)? Tell us (free-write) about it—down to the tiniest detail.

(after • words)
You can also use free writing whenever you're unsure of what to say or how to say it. Free writing often leads you to say things you didn't realize were on your mind—and to say them in an interesting way.

CLUSTERING

CLUSTERING STRATEGY

You probably already use **clustering** *as a prewriting strategy. If not, anyone who has can tell you what a great way it is to gather your thoughts about a writing topic. Clustering allows you to write down everything you know about a topic and then organize those details quickly and simply.*

"And now, a few words from our sponsor . . ."

Do a cluster in the space below on the topic of commercials—either your favorite or least favorite commercials. Add whatever words, ideas, or details come to mind when you think of these commercials. Don't stop to "choose" the best words; simply write down whatever comes to mind. (Turn to the "Clustering" section in your handbook for more information and a model.) The first circle is provided, but you may want to use your own paper for your cluster.

commercials

(after • words)
Now go back to your cluster and decide which commercial(s) and which details would work best for a short paper on commercials. Share your idea with your group or class.

LISTING

PREWRITING STRATEGY

Listing *is one of the most popular prewriting strategies because it is so direct and simple. It works especially well when you have plenty of ideas but need to see them down on paper before you begin*

Now, how do I get out of this one?

List 15 chores and tasks you hate. Cleaning your closet is an example of a chore you might hate. The thought of physical fitness tests in your gym class might also send shivers up your spine.

You'll never guess what happened to me!

Select one chore or task from your list, and on your own paper write a creative excuse explaining why you can't or haven't completed it. Make your excuse as original and wild as you want.

Note: A creative excuse usually isn't the first one which comes to mind. For example, no creativity is shown in the following well-worn excuse: "My dog ate my math assignment."

(after • words)
Use listing whenever you need to "see" the details inside your head before you begin writing. Once your details are listed, you can work them (arrange, add, cut) into a logical order.

COOPERATIVE LISTING

Wheel of Foolishness

You and a partner are participating in the popular game show *Wheel of Foolishness*, which offers you a chance to win the prizes of your dreams. What prizes would those be?

> **Write your prize choices below. Try alternating prize ideas. First, one of you list a prize, then the other. Work from each other's thinking. (Each of you should come up with at least three prizes.)**

1. _____

2. _____

3. _____

4. _____

5. _____

6. _____

Playing the Fool

> **The final winner of *Wheel of Foolishness* is the contestant who is willing to make the biggest fool of him- or herself. You and your partner should each list (on another sheet) three of the most ridiculous or embarrassing things you would do in order to win. (Maybe one of you would march through a popular shopping mall with a sign reading "Let's hear it for broccoli!")**

(after • words)
Even when you are not able to work directly with another person, listen carefully to what others come up with in their lists. Also, ask others for suggestions when your list is short and your mind is empty.

BRAINSTORMING

Solving Problems

▌ With your class or writing group, brainstorm and compile a list of **PROBLEMS** facing our world today. Think of problems students care most (or should care most) about.

▌ Choose one of these problems (or let your teacher choose one) and brainstorm for possible **CAUSES** of this problem.

▌ Finally, brainstorm for possible **SOLUTIONS**.

(after • words)
Brainstorming with a group will allow you to hear many possible ideas, more ideas than you would think of on your own. This strategy works well when you are asked to find several possible solutions to a problem.

STORY FRAMES

The Temple of Gloom

As a world-renowned adventurer, you've traveled to many exotic places and risked your life dozens of times . . . but you've never been involved in anything like this!

Read through the story frame below and supply appropriate words for the blanks. Remember that the words you choose will determine the direction your story takes. *Note:* Circle the appropriate him/her response according to your gender.

_____ (your name) raced into the room

and saw Dr. Drostmann chained to one of the

_____ (adjective) walls. She/he

_____ (adverb) approached his/her friend.

Just then, a large metal door on the far side of the room

screeched _____ (adverb) open, and in stepped

Forp! _____ (your name) looked around for a

_____ (noun) in the corner. If he/she acted

_____ (adverb), there was still hope. As

_____ (your name) moved to the corner, he/she

heard a strange _____ (noun), and immediately

found himself/herself in a _____ (adjective)

_____ (noun). It seemed like it would be

_____ (adverb) to get out. _____

(your name) decided that he/she needed a _____

(adjective) _____ (noun). Suddenly, _____

(name) appeared with a _____ (noun).

STORY STARTERS

PREWRITING STRATEGY

"Begin in the middle." As strange as this advice may sound, it is good advice, especially when you are writing a story. Start right in the middle of the action, just about the time the main character faces his greatest challenge. Later, you can go back and fill in the details that landed your character in this predicament.

Suddenly . . . !

Sara held a candle in one hand and clutched the stairway railing in her other. When she reached the bottom of the stairs, she listened again for the sound which seemed to come from the dining room. She went right for the china cabinet and set the candle on the top shelf. Suddenly, the cabinet slid away, and . . .

We are drawn right into the action in this passage since we join Sara as she descends the stairs. We share her uncertainty, and we wonder along with her *who or what is behind the cabinet*. We want to know what happens next. This suspense and uncertainty draw both the writer and the reader into the story.

Hook 'em good!

Write one or more of your own story starters, preferably for the type of story you generally like to read. Then write the rest of your story, or exchange story starters and write the rest of your classmate's story.

(after • words)
Use the story-starter strategy the next time you write a story or personal narrative. Also, collect good story ideas in your journal or learning log for future use.

IMAGINARY CONVERSATION

PREWRITING STRATEGY

The next time you just can't get started on a writing assignment, try creating an **imaginary conversation**. *Let the two people carry on a conversation about your topic; keep it going for as long as you can.*

Thanks for the tip!

Suppose you have just been asked to write a short paper evaluating your school. Use an imaginary conversation to get your thoughts flowing. Imagine that you've just received a phone call from a newcomer to your school. She or he wants to know what it's like in your school (what to expect, what to sign up or try out for, whom to make friends with, etc.). What will you tell this person?

_____ : *Hello.*
(your name)

_____ : *Hi, my name is _____ .*
(the newcomer's name)   *I'm new at school and . . .*

(after • words)
After you have taken this conversation as far as you possibly can, go back and star, circle, or underline those ideas you think you can use to write your assignment.

SCRAP WRITING

Toss it!

Make a writing scrap by crumpling a piece of your own paper so that it forms a compact, round shape. (Those of you who are inexperienced with scrap art might not be satisfied with your first creation. If this is the case, keep scrapping until you are satisfied.)

Scrap Heap

Fill in eight flat surfaces on your writing scrap with the letters which correspond to eight of the writing/thinking words in the list below. Any of the words in this list could help you develop ideas for a writing topic. (Read through the entire list before you make your choices.)

a. analyze	i. demonstrate	q. predict
b. compare	j. illustrate	r. review
c. define	k. praise	s. caution
d. group	l. remember	t. criticize
e. name	m. blame	u. exaggerate
f. rate	n. converse	v. improve
g. apply	o. describe	w. prove
h. contrast	p. imagine	x. twist

Scrap Art

TOSS: Select a favorite object to write about using your writing scrap. Then give your scrap a toss (not across the room, just a foot straight up), catch it, and record on your paper the letter (and corresponding writing word) which is most visible. **WRITE:** Then write nonstop for 3 to 5 minutes about your subject from the point of view of the writing word. **TOSS:** Continue tossing until you have written about your object from at least four points of view, which means you must toss your scrap at least four times.

(after • words)
Use scrap writing the next time you have to approach a topic in several different ways.

© 1995 Write Source Educational Publishing House, Box 460, Burlington, WI 53105

OBSERVING AND RECORDING

A Walking Tour

It may surprise you to know that many students have trouble writing, not because they lack the ability to write, but because they do not use their ability to *observe*. They simply do not "notice" the particular details about a person, place, or thing. Or they do not "concentrate" on the specific sights, sounds, smells, etc., that make one place or person different from the others.

■ Let's test your skills of observation. All you have to do is answer the following questions about the people, places, and things in your life.

1. What color is your house or apartment? What kind of material is it made of? How many floors or stories does it have?

2. Think about one of your closest neighbors. How tall would you say he or she is? How does your neighbor wear his or her hair? What does this person do for a living? What do you often see this person doing "around the neighborhood"?

3. What color are the walls of your kitchen? your living room? your bedroom? Describe in 10 words or less the floor in your school cafeteria.

4. What is one of the first things a person would see if she or he walked into your neighborhood grocery store?

Now that your awareness for detail has been heightened, go for a walk in your neighborhood and record those details that you somehow never noticed before: the large crack in the sidewalk, the oddly colored shed down the street, the beautiful flower garden across the road, the smell from the factory a few blocks away, etc.

Next, write up a list of questions from your observations that some (or all) of the kids in your class *should* be able to answer, were they to take the same walk through your neighborhood.

(after • words)
Keep a journal of things you observe from day to day. Often you will come across "found ideas," ideas which you find accidentally as you are observing. These ideas often make excellent writing topics.

FORMS OF WRITING

Writing Inside and Out

(fore•words) In the **Forms of Writing** activities, you'll write about things that we generally associate with "writing on the inside"—school-related writing. You'll be asked to write about personal experiences and about different people, places, and events. You'll also be asked to write a book review, a how-to paragraph, and a comparison and contrast paragraph.

But don't be surprised if, along the way, you are asked to write some things that are a little bit different and generally associated with "writing on the outside"—in the real world. For example, one activity asks you to write a survival guide; another activity asks you to write a letter to a publisher.

Taken as a whole, working on these activities will expand your writing knowledge, stimulate your thinking, and provide you with more than a little entertainment along the way.

Special Note: Your handbook "catalogs" a variety of important writing forms. Review the table of contents and see for yourself.

User's Checklist

Check your progress as you work on these **Forms of Writing.**

☐   **Autobiographical Experiences** • *Look, Mom, no hands!*

☐   **Writing About People** • *It sounds like Aunt Fannie . . .*

☐   **Writing About a Place** • *The Great Outdoors*

☐   **Writing a Guide** • *Survival of the Fittest!*

☐   **Letter Writing** • *And the winner is . . .*

☐   **Writing Book Reviews** • *As Easy As 1-2-3*

☐   **How-to Paragraphs** • *Just follow these few "easy" steps.*

☐   **Comparison and Contrast Writing** • *You two . . . come with me.*

☐   **Story Writing** • *The Missing Link*

☐   **Writing About an Event** • *I'll never forget . . .*

(after • words) One form of writing that we strongly recommend that you practice is personal journal writing. We know that the key to real improvement is writing on a regular basis. And there's no better way to write regularly than in your own journal. (See "Journal Writing" in your handbook for more information.)

AUTOBIOGRAPHICAL EXPERIENCES

Look, Mom, no hands!

Have you ever watched someone do something and thought, "That looks sooooo easy. I can do that." Then you tried and failed, and wondered how something could look so easy and be so difficult? Recall such a moment in your life and complete the autobiographical sketch below.

One day, when I was _____ , I decided to _____ .

It looked so easy. I thought all you had to do was _____

_____ .

Boy, was I mistaken. Let me tell you how wrong I was . . . _____

_____

_____

_____

_____

_____

_____

_____

_____

_____

_____

(after • words) Recall a time when you taught someone (a friend, a brother, a sister) how to do something. Write a brief autobiographical sketch about this experience.

WRITING ABOUT PEOPLE

It sounds like Aunt Fannie . . .

We have all read biographies or magazine articles about famous people: Babe Ruth, Abraham Lincoln, Martin Luther King, Mother Teresa, Billy Jo Smith . . . Billy Jo Smith? Well, maybe not Billy Jo. Billy Jo, you see, is a student just like you, but he has already done some remarkable things in his life. For example, he once caught a frog with his bare hands and taught it to jump. He was also a member of the winning air band in last year's talent show.

Do you know someone like Billy Jo? Without mentioning names, write about one of his or her significant or interesting experiences.

Don't tell your class who your subject is until after you've read your story to them. Let them try to guess. Even if it's no one they know, you'll be surprised at how many guesses they will make. (Use the space below to get started.)

NOTE: Use good judgment in what you say. You don't want to hurt anyone's feelings.

(after • words) Submit a fictitious name for a biographical writing activity. Draw one of these names from a hat and write about a significant or interesting experience from this person's life. Share your results.

WRITING ABOUT A PLACE

The Great Outdoors

Select a favorite or familiar outdoor spot to write about. It could be a park, a secret hiding place, or a sports arena. Whatever it is, you will want to describe it so your reader can visualize it. Fill in the "Prewriting Forum" below using the guidelines for "Writing About a Place" in your handbook.

PREWRITING FORUM
Topic or Place:
Observe
Helpful Hint: Close your eyes and try to imagine yourself in this place if you are not able to actually go there.
Investigate Define Describe Recall Compare Analyze Evaluate

(after • words) Write a "Phrase Poem" about this place. (See your handbook for help.)

WRITING A GUIDE

Survival of the Fittest!

Write a survival guide for someone who must live through what you have just lived through. Possible topics might be how to survive the first day of school, or trying out for something, or wearing braces, or going to the doctor or dentist, or . . . Then, find someone to give your survival guide to, someone who can actually use it.

Note: Your guide should be at least eight pages long. (Use one sheet of 8½- x 11-inch paper folded twice, stapled, and trimmed so that it opens like a book or guide.) You must have at least one survival tip per page.

How to Survive . . .

Helpful HINT

Write your tips on regular paper first; then rewrite them into your "book."

LETTER WRITING

And the winner is . . .

Congratulations! You have just received a letter announcing you as the winner of the $5,000,000 *Reader's Digest* Sweepstakes. The only problem is . . . you have to be eighteen years old to claim the prize. BOOOO!

Complete the following letter addressed to the publisher's marketing director. (Use your own paper.) Explain the problem; then try to convince him that although you are too young to claim the prize, he should give you something to make up for your great disappointment.

Your address

Date

Mr. John Bohane, Marketing Director
Reader's Digest
Reader's Digest Road
Pleasantville, New York 10570

Dear Mr. Bohane:

Today I received your letter informing me that I am the grand sweepstakes $5,000,000 winner. I think a mistake has been made . . . (*finish this thought*).

Although I cannot keep the prize, I think you . . . (*finish this thought*).

I would also be willing to sell my sad story to your magazine.

Please consider my request as soon as possible. I just found out that . . . (*finish this thought*), and I could really use the money.

Sincerely,

Your signature

(after • words) Congratulations! You have just completed one of your first business letters. Now go back and label the parts of the letter.

WRITING BOOK REVIEWS

As Easy As 1-2-3

Let's say you finished a book you enjoyed, and you want to convince others to read it, too. One way is to write a book review.

1 **Gathering Ideas**
Fold a piece of paper into four columns. Label each column with one of the following elements: *plot, character, setting,* and *theme.* Then list details about your book in the appropriate columns. For example, details about the action or excitement in the book would be listed under *plot.*

2 **Selecting the Topic**
Go to "The Book Review" section of your handbook. Read through "Finding an Idea for Your Review." Choose one of these ideas to be the subject of your book review. (Select an idea that matches up well with the details listed in one of your columns.)

● Turn this idea into a clear sentence that applies to your book. This will be the topic sentence of your book review. (Write the final version of this sentence here.)

_____

_____

_____

_____

3 **Writing the First Draft**
Now write a one-paragraph review on your own paper.
● Begin with your topic sentence, and follow with related details from one column in your list. Consider saving the most important detail for last. Add a closing sentence if necessary. (See the "One-Paragraph Book Review" model in your handbook.)
● Review and revise your writing.

(after • words) Share your finished review with a small group of classmates. Then ask them to give the "thumbs up" sign if you convinced them to read the book.

HOW-TO PARAGRAPHS

Just follow these few "easy" steps.

Write a *how-to* paragraph. You might write about how to make your favorite food, how to perform a certain stunt on your skateboard, or how to please your mother or father. Whatever you choose as the subject of your paragraph, make sure you know all the steps in the process.

First Do This . . . In the space provided below, list the steps for your how-to paragraph. Make sure you organize your list in the best possible order before you start writing your paragraph.

Next Do This . . . Develop your paragraph on your own paper. Make sure to use transitions like *first, second, finally,* etc., to move from one step to the next in your paragraph. Pay special attention to your word choices. Words like *carefully* and *slowly* and *immediately* make the directions clear to your reader.

(after • words) Present a how-to pantomime which demonstrates the subject of your writing. Follow the steps as you have them listed in your paragraph.

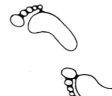

COMPARISON AND CONTRAST WRITING

You two . . . come with me.

▎ Select two people (with their approval, of course), two pets (approval not required), two objects (ditto), two places, two fruits, two kitchen utensils, two anything as subjects for this activity. The more interesting the subjects, the better. Identify your subjects on the lines provided below:

1. _____   2. _____

A New VENNture

▎ Now think and write about your subjects using the overlapping circles (called a Venn diagram) as your guide. In area number 1, list words and phrases that describe only subject number one. In area number 2, list words and phrases that describe only subject number two. Now comes the interesting part: In area number 3, list those things the two subjects have in common.

Note: Do some preliminary listing of ideas on your own paper to get a feel for your subjects before you list ideas in the diagram.

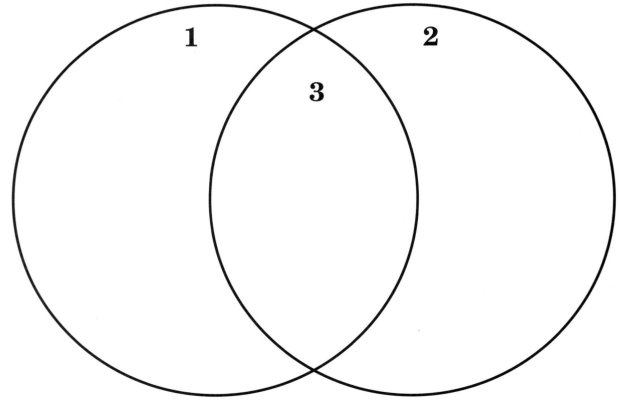

(after • words) Develop a comparison and contrast paragraph from the ideas in your diagram. Remember "compare" refers to how things are *alike*. "Contrast" refers to how they are *different*.

STORY WRITING

The Missing Link

Your favorite mystery writer has writer's block. He must have a mystery story finished by tomorrow, so he needs your help. You devise a plan—a "pass-along" mystery story. You start by writing the beginning to the story. Then you pass your beginning to another student. This student writes a middle and passes it to a third student who writes the ending. Use the opening sentence and the list of clues below to help you get started:

Suspects:	the family dog, the retired teacher, the ice-cream man, the new stranger in town, the maid
Victim:	the family, the seventh-grade students, you, the neighbor's cat, the butler
Clues:	a missing steak, a missing shoe, a chewed boot, a missing school bell, a missing broom, a broken window, footprints, a piece of white material, an old shoe, missing money

In spite of the driving rain, I was determined to get to the old mansion . . .

_____

_____

_____

_____

_____

_____

_____

_____

_____

Continue on your own paper.

(**after • words**) Revise and edit your story with your two co-authors. Share your mystery story with the other groups in your class.

WRITING ABOUT AN EVENT

I'll never forget . . .

All of us have at one time in our life witnessed an event that was exciting or unusual, one that will stick with us for a long time. It may have been a field trip, a parade, or a celebration. Maybe it was a live concert, play, or sporting event. Or maybe it was a rare natural event like an eclipse, a display of the northern lights, or a tornado. Perhaps it was something as simple as a family reunion or gathering of friends. Whatever it was, it would be a wonderful event to share with your readers.

> **Write about this event. Try to arrange the details of your story in a way that will build suspense or anticipation for your reader. (See "Writing About an Event" in your handbook for suggestions.)**

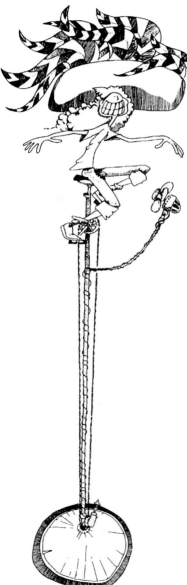

(after • words) Add an illustration or two to give your story added appeal.

REVISING WORKSHOPS

Getting Started

Connecting and Correcting Your Ideas

(fore•words) Whatever you write (including the last note you passed to a friend) is a direct reflection of your very own thinking. It only makes sense that you would want your words to reflect a positive image. After all, who doesn't want to look good?

Think of the workshops in this section as a series of "grooming tips"—each one designed to improve the quality and appearance of your writing. This focus of these activities is revising—that important step in the process that helps you turn first drafts into inviting pieces of writing. You will practice reviewing and revising paragraphs, learn about adding details to writing, work with figurative language, and more.

Special Note: Your handbook has a lot to say about revising so make sure you turn to it whenever you have a question about changing parts of a first draft. (Refer to "Revising" in the index for this information.)

User's Checklist

Check your progress as you work on these **Revising Workshops.**

☐ **Reviewing First Drafts** • *A Matter of Choice*

☐ **Reviewing a Paragraph** • *Open at your own risk!*

☐ **Reviewing and Revising Paragraphs** • *That's a foul!*

☐ **Supporting Important Ideas** • *Keeping Fit*

☐ **Adding Details** • *Haven't I heard that before?*

☐ **Showing Versus Telling** • *It's show time!*

☐ **Using Figurative Language** • *I am cool like a saxophone.*

(after • words) Working hard at your writing—whether it be in these practice workshops or in a writing assignment—is a *no lose* situation. You'll feel better about your writing ability, your classmates will appreciate reading what you produce, and your teachers will reward you for your efforts.

REVIEWING FIRST DRAFTS

A Matter of Choice

(fore • words) What makes for good writing? Five basic points appear on the lists of most writing experts: Good writing displays . . .

- originality in the choice or approach to a subject,
- effective organization of ideas,
- colorful words and details,
- clear and smooth-flowing sentences, and
- a clear and "correct" final product.

Some writers stress the importance of writing with a clear purpose and audience in mind. The bottom line for other writers is the enjoyment or informational value of the writing. What makes writing work for you? Let's find out.

Carefully read the sample paragraphs that follow. (All three are sections of personal student writing.) Underline _____ words or ideas that you especially like. Draw a wavy line ﹏﹏﹏﹏ under words or ideas that confuse or bother you. Then rank the paragraphs, putting a "1" next to the paragraph you like best and so on.

Note: Base your ranking on the markings you have made, the qualities of good writing described above, and/or a reviewing checklist supplied by your teacher.

About five minutes before the bell rang, my teacher told us that *Peter Pan* would be on TV that night. I was so excited that when she dismissed us I ran out the door forgetting all about beating up Jimmy. When I got home, I told my mom that *Peter Pan* was going to be on. She didn't seem all that interested. All through dinner I was restless. I spilled my milk two times, and I could tell that my parents were getting a little upset. When the movie actually started, it must have been the first time I was quiet in eight hours. My favorite part of the movie was right at the end when Peter Pan flew out of the children's window. I asked my parents if I could fly. They said sure, just sprinkle some magic dust from the wall on yourself. I did that and immediately leaped off the couch. Of course, I landed flat on my face. My parents had a good laugh over that one.

☐ In preparation for our class trip to the circus, our class worked for weeks on a circus train made of shoe boxes. One day while working on our train, Carrie Kaske said her mom fainted when she saw the lion tamer at her first circus. When the day for our trip finally came, my wonderful circus turned out to be one disappointment after another. I couldn't see why Carrie's mom got so upset over the lion tamer. I couldn't see him at all. I couldn't see much of anything for that matter. We were so far away from the action that I could barely make out anything. After the first half hour, all I wanted to do was buy a Pepsi and a monkey-on-a-stick and get out of there. Of course, nothing in life is that easy. Our room mothers had thoughtfully brought cartons of warm milk along for us to drink. I remember returning to school tired and a little wiser. I looked at our little circus train, and felt much better about it than I did about the real circus.

☐ My sixth grade class at Raymond School was fun because of the things we did to get the teacher mad. I can remember the time I threw clay balls on the ceiling. The teacher asked me why I did it, and I said I didn't know. The weird thing about it is I didn't get in trouble. Or the time Brian Battisti dropped the handle for the drinking fountain down the sink. He told the teacher that somebody loosened it, and when he pulled on it, it fell into the sink. The thing that got the teachers really mad was the time Brian and I soaped the fountain. The taste didn't go away for a month.

(after • words) Share the results of your ranking with your classmates. Then, write about the reasons for one of your choices in a brief paragraph. In your writing, refer to specific things you liked or disliked in the selection.

REVIEWING A PARAGRAPH

Open at your own risk!

> Read the paragraph below. Draw a straight line under words and ideas you like. Draw a wavy line under words and ideas that need work. Then, in the spaces provided, tell what you think are the paragraph's strengths and weaknesses. Make at least one observation in each category. (The "Commenting on Writing" checklist at the end of "Group Advising" will help you make your remarks. Also, refer to your handbook for information about topic sentences.)

My locker is messy. When you open it, books and papers fall out. It contains papers from the beginning of the school year, which was four months ago. My locker is so messy it would be easier to find a needle in a haystack than a pencil in my locker. If a man from the Environmental Protection Agency came to look at my locker, he would put up a sign saying: Stop! Do not open! Disaster zone! I am surprised I haven't found anything alive in there yet. Sometimes I wonder if my brush is in there. I have been looking for it for three weeks. However, I love the lived-in look.

Topic sentence: _____

_____

Purpose and voice: _____

_____

Content and form: _____

_____

Writing devices and sentence style: _____

_____

_____

Overall strengths and weaknesses: _____

_____

_____

(after • words) Share your observations with your classmates. *Remember:* Not everyone "sees" the same things in a piece of writing.

REVIEWING AND REVISING PARAGRAPHS

That's a foul!

(fore • words) When we write freely and rapidly, we let our thoughts run wild, so to speak. When we write a paragraph, however, we are more disciplined and keep our thoughts under better control. A well-written paragraph displays a logical and orderly development of thought. When that logic and order are tampered with, readers cry, "Foul!" And that's what you should do (to yourself, of course) after reading the paragraph below.

Read the following paragraph carefully. Put a star (*) in front of the sentence that would make the best topic sentence. Put check marks (✔) in front of three sentences which support the topic sentence. And put an ex (X) in front of two sentences which do not relate to the topic sentence. (Share your results.)

___ Instead of becoming an invalid, she studied hard and became a teacher. ___ Jill Kinmont overcame a very serious handicap and made an important contribution to education. ___ Formal public-school education usually begins in kindergarten. ___ At the age of 18, Jill was paralyzed from the shoulders down in a skiing accident. ___ Spring skiing is a lot of fun. ___ As a teacher, she developed a new program to help children read more easily.

(after • words) On your own paper, rewrite the model paragraph so it is orderly and logical. Select the best order for the three supporting sentences, and add your own closing sentence. (See the chapter on paragraphs in your handbook if you have any questions.)

Special Challenge: Write your own mixed-up paragraph that would cause a reader to cry "Foul!" Exchange your writing with a classmate, and straighten out each other's mess. (Share your results.)

SUPPORTING IMPORTANT IDEAS

Keeping Fit

(fore • words) There's a certain level of detail that readers expect in a piece of writing. When a point is made, they expect it to be supported with specific examples and details before the next important point is made.

The act of "presenting" readers with important ideas and then "supporting" those ideas with details is the foundation for almost all types of writing. Writing without supporting detail is like trying to bake a loaf of bread without yeast—one of the most important ingredients is missing.

Below is a skeleton of a basic paragraph. That is, it contains a topic sentence followed by three important points. The paragraph lacks supporting ideas and details.

> **Put the following paragraph in proper balance by adding supporting ideas and details after each major point. Space has been provided for your planning. Write your expanded paragraph on your own paper. *Note:* Two supporting ideas have been listed after the first major point to get you started.**

Physical fitness tests bring out the worst (best) in me. (1) I'm able to manage with a few of the tests. (2) Others push my physical ability and my pride to the limits. (3) I may as well not even try when it comes to one fitness test.

1. *The 100-yard dash is easy enough.* (What details could support this idea?) _____

For some reason I can match sit-ups with some of my classmates. (What details could support this idea?) _____

2. _____

_____

_____

3. _____

_____

(after • words) Exchange paragraphs with a classmate and evaluate the "fitness" of each other's writing. In the future, check all of your writing for balance between important points and supporting detail. Make changes in sections that are out of proper balance.

ADDING DETAILS

Haven't I heard that before?

(fore • words) While you review a piece of your writing, you may come across an idea or a sentence that seems especially dead and flat. Study the idea carefully. It might contain one of those overused figures of speech we call cliches.

Look up "cliche" in the index of *Write Source 2000* and locate a definition and examples. When you stumble across these tired figures of speech in your own writing, replace them with living details, details that hit the exact point you want to make.

The following three sentences contain cliches. Underline the cliche in each. After each sentence list details that would make those sentences come alive. Think in terms of the 5 W's (who? what? when? where? and why?) of writing plus sensory, memory, and reflective details. (Refer to "Details, Kinds of" in your handbook index for help.)

1. Mr. Shaw, our math teacher, is as <u>sharp as a tack</u>.

2. Running back Jerome Overstreet is as <u>strong as an ox</u>.

3. I <u>split a gut</u> whenever I go out with _____ .

(after • words) Rework one of the sentences into a full, detailed paragraph without cliches. (Make changes in the names or setting of the sentence if that will make it easier to write about.) Be sure your paragraph has a clear main point and contains plenty of "showing" detail.

SHOWING VERSUS TELLING

It's show time!

(fore • words) Do you remember when you were in kindergarten and you played show-and-tell? You would wait all day long to reveal your incredible, unbeliev-able, never-before-seen treasure only to stand tongue-tied before the class. Well, writing is a little like show-and-tell; you want to draw a lively, powerful picture for your reader without getting tongue-tied. Read on and see how one writer "shows" in her writing.

Writer Shirley Jackson knows exactly what it means to show in writing, to create effective images (word pictures) that help a reader see parts of the story in his or her mind. In her famous short story "Charles," Ms. Jackson doesn't tell us that Charles was a naughty boy at school; she lets his actions speak for themselves:

> **Telling Sentence:** Charles continued to be naughty for the rest of the week.

> **Showing Writing:** The third day—it was Wednesday of the first week—Charles bounced a seesaw onto the head of a little girl and made her bleed, and the teacher made him stay in for recess. Thursday Charles had to stand in a corner during story time because he kept pounding his feet on the floor. Friday Charles was deprived of blackboard privileges because he threw chalk.

It's your turn. Select one of the telling sentences that follow and remake it into a showing paragraph on your own paper. (Share your results.)

The roller coaster was scary.

The room was messy.

_____ drives me crazy.

Yesterday was a disaster.

The pizza tastes good.

(Your own telling sentence.)

Helpful Hint: How do you "show" in writing? Think in terms of the 5 W's and H (who? what? when? where? why? and how?). Your writing should answer some (if not all) of these questions. Also, think in terms of sensory, memory, and reflective details. (See "Details, Kinds of" in the handbook index.)

(after • words) Exchange something with a classmate that you have recently writ-ten. Note sentences in each other's paper that could be improved with more "showing." Select one sentence to expand into showing writing once your paper is returned.

USING FIGURATIVE LANGUAGE

I am cool like a saxophone.

(fore • words) The best descriptive comparisons help a reader *see* what the writer sees, in a new and creative way.

      Instead of **"John is *as busy as a bee*,"** a perceptive writer would say, **"John darts through a day *like a bug on water*."** This is a more interesting and original comparison.

Here's an effective and easy way to write creative descriptions of your own. Complete the following statements which ask you to compare yourself to different things. In this exercise, honesty is the best policy—the comparisons should say something true about you.

     Example: If I were a car, I'd be a(n) _____ *Buick Regal* _____ because

_____ *it is known for its dependability* _____ .

1. If I were a musical instrument, I'd be a(n) _____ because

_____ .

2. If I were a color, I'd be the color _____ because

_____ .

3. If I were a food, I'd be a(n) _____ because

_____ .

4. If I were a piece of clothing, I'd be a(n) _____ because

_____ .

5. If I were a movie, I'd be a(n) _____ because

_____ .

Now that you've started describing the real you, try thinking of two of your own comparisons.

6. If I were a(n) _____ , I'd be a(n) _____ because

_____

_____ .

7. If I were a(n) _____ , I'd be a(n) _____ because

_____

_____ .

Tighten Up

Special Challenge: The descriptive comparisons you have just made could be stated more concisely in shorter similes or metaphors—the type of descriptive comparisons you should use in your own writing. For instance, the example comparison given on the previous page could be stated in the following two ways:

Simile: I'm as dependable as a _____*Buick Regal*_____ .

Metaphor: I'm a _____*Buick Regal*_____ when it comes to dependability.

Rewrite any two of your descriptive comparisons so that each one expresses a concise simile or metaphor. (Refer to your handbook for additional examples and an explanation.)

1. _____

_____

2. _____

_____

(after • words) Use one of your comparisons as the subject of a paragraph. Compare your results with your classmates' to see how they "extended" their comparisons in their writing.

SENTENCE-COMBINING WORKSHOPS

Connecting Your Ideas

(fore•words) When experienced writers are really on a roll, the words and ideas come pouring out—the faucet open full blast. They are so busy getting all of their ideas on paper that they don't have time to worry about the look or sound of their sentences. They save that job for later when they are ready to revise and edit their work. Then they pay special attention to their sentences, making sure each one flows smoothly. Any awkward-sounding ideas will be rewritten; any short, choppy sentences will be combined or expanded.

This section focuses on two important stylistic techniques: sentence combining and sentence expanding. In the first four workshops, you will practice sentence combining using different types of phrases and clauses. Then, in the final workshop, you will learn about expanding basic sentences using meaningful words and phrases. After completing these activities, you will be much better prepared to attend to the sentences in your own writing during revising and editing.

Special Note: Your handbook contains a lot of good information related to sentence combining and sentence style. (Refer to "Sentence" in the index for this information.)

Getting Started

User's Checklist

Check your progress as you work on these **Sentence-Combining Workshops.**

☐ **Combining Sentences with Phrases** • *Keyed Up*

☐ **Combining Sentences with Adverb Clauses** • *That's not so complex!*

☐ **Combining Sentences with Adjective Clauses** • *"We are gathered here to join . . ."*

☐ **Sentence-Combining Review** • *A Combination of Things*

☐ **Sentence Expanding** • *Pumping Life into Your Writing*

(after • words) The best way to improve your style is to write often, experimenting with a number of different forms and techniques. (Refer to the list of exercises at the end of the "Styling Sentences" chapter in your handbook for some creative ideas.)

COMBINING SENTENCES WITH PHRASES

Keyed Up

(fore • words) Experienced writers often combine short, simple sentences into longer, more meaningful ones by keying up on an important phrase in one of the sentences.

The following types of phrases are often the key when it comes to sentence combining: **prepositional**, **participial**, **infinitive**, and **appositive phrases**. Read about these phrases in your handbook, and use the reading as a guide when you work on the example sentences that follow. (See "Phrase, Combining with" in the index.)

Combine each pair of simple sentences using the phrase indicated in the parentheses. (The first one has been done for you.)

1. The movie is terrible. It is showing at the Hargrove Theater. (participial phrase)

   The movie showing at the Hargrove Theater is terrible.

2. Frank and Phil waited for their pizza. They are the famous Fettucini brothers. (appositive phrase)

   _____

   _____

3. Glenna tore into a jelly-filled doughnut. It was from the "chewy and gooey" shelf in the bakery. (prepositional phrases)

   _____

   _____

4. The beggar held the winning lottery ticket. The beggar was beaming with delight. (participial phrase)

   _____

   _____

5. Terrance studied each mountain bike. He wanted to determine which one best met his needs. (infinitive phrase)

_____

_____

6. Alex blew a hole in one of his basketball shoes. He was running down the court. (participial phrase)

_____

_____

7. Billie must be nuts. She agreed to baby-sit on a school night. (infinitive phrase)

_____

_____

8. Josie's hair can be uncontrollable. It is uncontrollable especially in wet weather. (especially + a prepositional phrase)

_____

_____

9. The Girls Next Door played at the last school dance. They are music's answer to apple pie and sugar cookies. (appositive phrase)

_____

_____

10. James shocked all of his classmates. He was reading from his most recent paper. (participial phrase)

_____

_____

(after • words) Read the opening page of "Combining Sentences" in your handbook. On another sheet of paper identify two things you learned. Also, identify one or more questions you have after reading this page. (Share your remarks with a classmate.)

COMBINING SENTENCES WITH ADVERB CLAUSES

That's not so complex!

(fore • words) Which words carry more meaning . . . words like *and, or,* and *but* or words like *after, although, before,* and *unless*? The answer to this question should be easy. The second set of words carries more meaning. These words are **subordinate conjunctions** and are used to form complex sentences. Use them in your own writing. (The first set of words are coordinate conjunctions. These words are used to form compound sentences, among other things.)

Subordinate conjunctions introduce adverb clauses. Adverb clauses can be used at the beginning or at the end of complex sentences.

John checked the apple for wormholes. He ate the apple. (two simple sentences)

Before he ate the apple, *John checked it for wormholes.* (adverb clause at the beginning of the sentence—comma needed)

*John checked the apple for wormholes **before he ate it.*** (adverb clause at the end of the sentence—no comma needed)

▌ **Combine the following short sentences into one sentence using the conjunction listed in parentheses.**

1. I was about six years old.
   Something unforgettable happened. (*when*)

   _____

   _____

2. My dad banged on my bedroom door.
   He yelled, "Get dressed and get downstairs!" (*as*)

   _____

   _____

3. I realized I had forgotten my glasses.
   I was halfway down the stairs. (*before*)

   _____

   _____

4. "What's wrong?" I asked.
   I struggled to pull on my shoes. (*while*)

   _____

   _____

5. My dad turned and yelled, "Fire!"
   He rushed out the front door. (*as*)

   _____

   _____

6. He caught his breath.
   He said, "The neighbor's house is on fire." (*when*)

   _____

   _____

7. My heart was beating wildly in my throat.
   I was still half asleep. (*although*)

   _____

   _____

8. I was hit by a blast of hot, smokey wind.
   I followed my dad outside. (*as*)

   _____

   _____

9. I was awake by then.
   I still hoped this was all a dream. (*although*)

   _____

   _____

(after • words) Write a paragraph (or more) about fire. Maybe you have been involved in a fire. Maybe you have a fireplace or a relative who is a firefighter. Exchange your writing with a classmate. Read and enjoy each other's story. Then note ideas that might be combined using adverb clauses. Combine the ideas as indicated when you get your paper back. (Discuss the results.)

COMBINING SENTENCES WITH ADJECTIVE CLAUSES

"We are gathered here to join . . ."

(fore • words) Combining simple sentences using adjective clauses will help you avoid unnecessary repetition in your writing. (Adjective clauses begin with words like **who, whose, which,** and **that**.) But be careful. Too many "who's" or "which's" will make your writing sound textbookish.

Who, whose, which, and that are called relative pronouns. Find a definition of *relative pronoun* in your handbook and write it in the space provided below. (Also, read the example sentences in your handbook.)

Definition: *A relative pronoun is both a . . .*

Combine each pair of simple sentences into one complex sentence using *who, which,* and *that* as connectors. (Refer to the examples in your handbook for help.)
Note: **Key words and punctuation marks have already been put into place in many of the problems.**

1. The bearded wrestler gave his opponent a bear hug.
   The bearded wrestler was slick with sweat.

   The bearded wrestler, who _____ ,

   gave _____ .

2. The night air revived him after the day in the fields.
   The air was cool and sweet smelling.

   The night air, which _____ ,

   revived _____ .

3. The ancient oak was destroyed in the storm.
   It stood near the park entrance.

   The ancient oak that _____

   was _____ .

4. The construction workers were treated for heat exhaustion.
   They were building the new road past the park.

   The construction workers who _____

   _____.

5. The sun is the center of our solar system.
   The sun is 93 million miles away.

   _____ *, which* _____ ,

   _____.

6. The tracks led to the old miner's shack.
   The tracks were freshly made.

   The tracks, which _____ ,

   _____ *shack*

7. By the side of the road lay the ruined glider.
   The glider had been destined for Paris.

   _____ *glider*

   that _____.

8. The agents escaped across the border.
   The agents set Mr. Goodwin free.

   The agents who _____ *free*

   _____.

9. Rudy seldom checks out books.
   He would rather rap than read.

   Rudy, who _____ ,

   _____.

(after • words) Many of the complex sentences you have made contain commas. (The commas set off the adjective clause from the rest of the sentence.) Read about **restrictive** and **nonrestrictive clauses** in your handbook and find out why. Write your explanation on your own paper.

Commas are used to set off adjective clauses when . . .

SENTENCE-COMBINING REVIEW

A Combination of Things

(fore • words) Combining short, simple sentences into longer, more meaningful ones cures an ailment (illness) that, at times, "disables" young writers. This ailment is primer-style writing—writing that sounds stiff and choppy. The sentence-combining activities you have practiced so far have provided you with a variety of cures for this ailment. Put these "cures" to good use in this review activity and in all of your writing.

Complete the two sentence-combining activities that follow. (Make sure to share your work with your classmates.)

■ **Combine the set of four short sentences into longer, smoother-reading ones. (Follow the sentence "frames" when they are provided for you.)**

> Jolene is an unusual girl.
> She performs at school assemblies.
> She recites from *Webster's Collegiate Dictionary*.
> It is a book of 1,563 pages that she has memorized.

Frame 1: Jolene _____ girl

who _____

by reciting _____ ,

a book _____ .

Frame 2: Jolene, an unusual _____ ,

performs _____

by _____ ,

a _____ .

Frame 3: (See if you can come up with your own version.)

◼ **Combine the following sets of simple sentences, and then on your own paper finish the story. (The first combined sentence has been done for you.)**

Jerri thought tryouts were a lot easier last year.
She was a seventh grader then.

Jerri thought tryouts were a lot easier last year when she was a seventh grader.

She had thought for sure she had made the team.
The coach did cut her.

_____

_____

She wondered now if Coach Anderson didn't like her.
He always seemed to yell at her.

_____

_____

Jerri then thought something different.
Maybe the coach was trying to help her.

_____

_____

The practice lasted another 30 minutes.
Coach Anderson stopped practice.

_____

_____

He told the players to take a shower.
He told them to check the bulletin board on their way out.
A list of players who made the second cut would be posted.

_____

_____

Jerri headed for the showers. She . . . *(Finish on your own paper.)*

(after • words) Exchange stories with a classmate. Check each other's work for primer-style or choppy writing.

SENTENCE EXPANDING

Pumping Life into Your Writing

(fore • words) Let's say you are really serious about weight lifting or aerobic dancing—I mean really serious—and you want to learn as much as you can about either of these forms of exercise. What should you do? Obviously, working with a professional, someone who has studied and practiced long hours, would be a good idea. That's what we are going to ask you to do in this activity.

No, you're not going to study bodybuilding or dance. But you are going to study the work of professional writers who have worked long hours at their craft. Read on and find out why.

Very Interesting, Very Interesting Indeed

Good writers have a special knack for wording things in just the right way. They can expand ideas with words and phrases that add detail, that search out meaning in a way that makes their writing work for us. We get so caught up in the smooth flow of their thoughts that the actual words and sentences they use almost become invisible.

> **Study the sentences that follow. Read them out loud or have a partner read them to you. Listen and enjoy. See how these authors expand basic sentences (in boldface) to add meaning to their writing. (Also, make sure that you read "Styling Sentences" in your handbook for more examples.)**

● Details added after the basic sentence:

> **He looks different**, a little less like camp, a little more dressed up.
>
> From *There's a Bat in Bunk Five* by Paula Danzinger

> **Wil nodded to himself and slipped away**, softly as a mouse, toward the back of the house where the tourists were never taken.
>
> From "A Room Full of Leaves" by Joan Aiken

● Details added before the basic sentence:

> Staring at the unblemished blue of the sky, listening to the children shout, "Rise, Sally rise. Sally, wipe your pretty eyes," **I turned that question over in my mind.**
>
> From *The Friends* by Rosa Guy

If the food was bad, favored by an excellent digestion, **he ate it anyway**.
If his surroundings were gloomy and the company either boring to him
or nonexistent, **he did not fidget**.

> From "Total Stranger" by James Gould Cozzens

● Details added before and after the basic sentence:

In the first sign of alarm, **he saw them clamber down the sapling
and slip away** to the west beyond the gullberries.

> From *The Yearling* by Marjorie Kinnan Rawlings

From then on, **it was like they were two dogs**, each waiting
for the other one to make a move and start the fight.

> From *Hoops* by Walter Dean Meyers

(after • thought) Decide which sentence you like the best, which one reads the most effortlessly, which one is expanded in the most meaningful way. (Discuss your findings with a classmate.)

It's your turn. Expand the two basic sentences that follow into longer, more meaningful thoughts: (Use the space provided.)

Connie began to laugh.

Charles turned quickly.

(after • words) Refer to one of the short stories you've read in class, an article in your favorite magazine, or a section in one of your favorite books, and find two expanded sentences that you really like. Underline the basic sentence and circle the words, phrases, and clauses that were used to expand it. (Compare your findings with those of a classmate.)

EDITING WORKSHOPS

Checking for Sentence and Usage Errors

(fore•words) You can accomplish a lot as a writer by following this basic rule: *Use clear and complete sentences.* Good writing, writing that effectively communicates an idea, is built on a foundation of clear and complete thoughts.

Your mind automatically tunes in to sentences. You read sentences, hear sentences, and even think sentences. And for the most part, you use effective sentences when you develop your writing. But every writer—including your favorite authors—may occasionally make mistakes. That is why it is so important to check your work for sentence errors before you write a final draft.

As you probably know, our language is full of homophones, words that are pronounced alike but are different in meaning or spelling. Words like *to, too,* and *two* are homophones. Using words like these correctly can be a real challenge. That is why it is also important to check your writing for usage errors.

The first set of **Editing Workshops** in this section will help you write clear, complete sentences. The second set of workshops deals with using the right word. By completing the work in this section, you will become better able to identify and correct these types of errors in your writing.

Getting Started

User's Checklist

Check your progress as you work on these **Editing Workshops.**

☐   **Editing for Clarity** • *"It's a Superflooz VII Intergalactic Spacezipper!"*

☐   **Editing for Smoothness, Clarity** • *An Egg-Sighting Experience!*

☐   **Eliminating Wordiness** • *Night Crawlers*

☐   **Correcting Sentence Fragments** • *Otter Facts and Fragments*

☐   **Correcting Comma Splices/Run-ons** • *Bamboozled*

☐   **Avoiding Rambling Sentences** • *And . . . and then . . . and . . .*

☐   **Using the Right Word 1** • *Camp Runamuck*

☐   **Using the Right Word 2** • *Independence Day*

☐   **Using the Right Word 3** • *Words of Wisdom*

☐   **Using the Right Word 4** • *Put it in writing!*

☐   **Using the Right Word—Review 1** • *. . . a dear little nuisance . . .*

☐   **Using the Right Word—Review 2** • *Get ready, get set (or is it sit?), go!*

(after • words)   Before you turn in a writing assignment, always have a trusted friend, classmate, or family member check your work for sentence and usage errors. All professional writers have editors who do the same. Why should you be any different?

EDITING FOR CLARITY

"It's a Superflooz VII Intergalactic Spacezipper!"

1. Read the paragraph below. It contains a number of words, phrases, and sentences which are unclear and could easily mislead the reader.
2. Locate one example of each type of error listed beneath the paragraph; write the number of the sentence in which you found each error on the blank provided. (Refer to your handbook index for help. Each type of error is listed there.)
3. Then correct each error in the paragraph itself. (Rewrite those sentences which need major revising on the lines provided.)

(1) Learning to pilot a Superflooz VII Intergalactic Spacezipper at ultra-light speed is really much easier than it sounds. (2) First, the pilot must strap himself into the control seat so he can't hardly move. (3) Then he must switch on the viewing screen. (4) This special screen nearly allows the pilot to see for five miles. (5) At this point, the pilot must switch on the Magno-Zip Atombooster. (6) This switch is located just above the pilot's head and looks sort of like a radish. (7) One of the switches are green and should not be touched at all, for it will activate the ship's destruct mechanism. (8) After warming up for three minutes, the pilot can throw the switch for the Magno-Zip Atombooster to the no-return position. (9) The pilot must remember not to overload their Magno-Zip Atombooster. (10) If he follows all of these directions carefully, it should be a smooth trip.

_____ Double negative   _____ Pronoun problem (agreement)

_____ Misplaced modifier (one word)   _____ Misplaced modifier (phrase)

_____ Agreement of subject and verb

Revised Sentences: _____

_____

_____

(after • words) Refer to the two pages in your handbook that begin with "Problems with Pronouns" ("Pronoun, Problems" in your index). Make note of one "problem" on either page that wasn't covered in this activity. Also, note how to correct the problem. (Discuss your results.)

EDITING FOR SMOOTHNESS, CLARITY

An Egg-Sighting Experience!

(fore • words) All writing should read smoothly and move clearly (logically) from one point to the next. Linking or transitional words like *also, finally,* and *later* and the repetition of key words or phrases can help make your writing smooth reading and clear.

> **Many of the linking words have been taken out of the paragraph below. Read the paragraph and fill in the blanks as you go with a linking word or expression which helps the paragraph flow smoothly from one point to the next. Share your results. (See "Transitions" in your handbook index for a list of linking words.)**

When I was younger, I was always begging my parents to let me cook something

by myself. _____ my father said he'd teach me how to fry an egg. What a

mess. _____ we got out all the dishes and utensils we needed—a frying

pan, pot holder, spatula, cup, plate, and a fork. _____ we got the eggs

and margarine from the refrigerator. _____ accidentally smashing one

egg on the floor and letting one roll into the sink, I finally managed to crack an egg into

the cup and throw the shell in the garbage—after one miss. _____ I

heated a little margarine in the frying pan and slowly poured the egg from the cup into

the pan. Flipping the egg over when it was done on one side was the hardest part.

Melted margarine sure knows how to splatter. _____ , when it was time

to lift my breakfast out of the pan, I discovered how slippery fried eggs are.

_____ a few tries, I did manage to slide that over-easy egg onto the

plate, but there was nothing easy about it. _____ it was time to eat.

_____ cooking was more work than I had expected, that egg tasted great!

ELIMINATING WORDINESS

Night Crawlers

(fore • words) One of the most popular books on writing for writers of all ages is entitled *Elements of Style.* The authors of that book stress the importance of simplicity in writing. How do you achieve simplicity in writing? By giving the axe to any words or phrases that don't add to or strengthen the purpose of your writing.

As you read the model paragraph, cross out any words that are unnecessary. (Some sentences can be corrected in more than one way.) The first sentence is done for you.

(1) It was late—time to go to sleep if we wanted to get up ~~early~~ at 4:00 a.m. ~~in the morning~~ for some good fishing. (2) But we needed worms and were too excited to sleep, which goes without saying. (3) We carefully slid the patio door open with great care, trying hard to keep quiet and not make any noise either. (4) There was a light fog that seemed to cling to everything it touched. (5) Closing the door slowly, we stepped softly onto the patio. (6) My friend, he turned on his flashlight so we could see better in the haze. (7) We found the worm-holding box on a shelf and headed for the flower garden, walking toward it from the house. (8) I flashed my flashlight at the moist ground and spotted a couple of fat night crawlers slipping back into their holes and sliding under the ground to escape. (9) My friend grabbed them just in time and dropped them into the box. (10) On we went, shining our lights and grabbing worms until we had plenty of bait that would be enough for a morning of fishing. (11) My friend and I, we were tired as we put everything away and snuck back to our room, finally ready to get some rest before our fishing trip.

(after • words) Your writing is a reflection of your very own thinking. To make sure that your writing reflects favorably on you, keep it clear and to the point. Check at least one of your most recent writings and eliminate any unnecessary words you may have included.

CORRECTING SENTENCE FRAGMENTS

Otter Facts and Fragments

(fore • words) A sentence is more than a random collection of words and phrases, just as an airplane is more than a pile of parts and pieces. (Neither will "fly" with parts missing.)

A sentence must contain a subject and a predicate (verb) which are arranged with other words into a complete thought. A sentence that does not express a complete thought is called a **sentence fragment**. ("Fragment sentence" in your handbook index will refer you to information and examples.)

Identify the following groups of words by writing S for each sentence or F for each fragment on the line before each.

Example: _S_ River otters are slender, water animals.

         _F_ Are related to weasels and mink. *(no subject)*

         _F_ While the otters live in burrows along the rivers. *(dependent clause)*

_____ 1. The otter's oily fur, which forms a waterproof coat.

_____ 2. River otters were once common all over North America; even so, outdoorsmen rarely saw them.

_____ 3. Are wary of humans.

_____ 4. Chattering noisily, they take turns sliding down snowy banks and belly flopping into the water.

_____ 5. Webbed toes and strong tails make otters excellent swimmers.

_____ 6. Paddling with their feet and using their strong tails to steer.

_____ 7. Prized for its rich fur like their relative the mink.

_____ 8. During the 1880's, the otter was trapped heavily and began to disappear.

_____ 9. Recently, pollution and fewer wetlands have reduced the otter's numbers.

_____ 10. Are now a protected species with state programs to help them.

(after • words) Exchange a piece of writing in progress with a partner and check it for fragments.

CORRECTING COMMA SPLICES/RUN-ONS

Bamboozled

(fore • words) A **comma splice** occurs when you incorrectly connect two simple sentences with a comma instead of a period, semicolon, or connecting word. A **run-on sentence** occurs when you incorrectly join two simple sentences without punctuation or a connecting word. Both types of errors can be avoided if you carefully review each of your sentences before sharing your writing with your readers. (Refer to "Comma, Splice" and "Run-on sentence" in your handbook index for more information and examples.)

▎ **Place a CS in front of each comma splice, an RO in front of each run-on sentence, and a C in front of each correct sentence. Correct each faulty sentence.**

_CS_ 1. Bamboo is definitely one of the most interesting plants,ₐ*and* it is valued for its beauty and utility.

_____ 2. Bamboo may be one of the world's most useful plants.

_____ 3. Bamboo grows in huge groves it serves as a natural protection against flood erosion and earthquake shock.

_____ 4. In addition, bamboo adds to the soil's richness.

_____ 5. Man has found bamboo indispensable he uses it for building, for musical instruments, and for furniture.

_____ 6. Bamboo is also an important food source, its crisp texture makes it a favorite in oriental cooking.

_____ 7. Bamboo is interesting not only to the common man, but it is also interesting to scientists.

_____ 8. This plant is a member of the grass family it grows naturally on every continent except Europe and Antarctica.

_____ 9. About a thousand different species of bamboo exist, differing widely in color, shape, and size.

_____ 10. Bamboo varies greatly in size, some varieties grow to the height of field grass while others reach heights of over 100 feet.

_____ 11. All bamboo plants have wood stalks known as culms.

_____ 12. The culm is usually round, hollow, and jointed, it makes the plant unusually strong.

_____ 13. One of the most interesting features of bamboo is its growth speed nothing grows as tall and as rapidly as bamboo.

_____ 14. In Japan a common type of bamboo is known to have grown four feet in 24 hours.

_____ 15. At this rate, the stalk's growth would likely be visible an observer, however, would have to be extremely patient.

(after • words) Sometimes it's easier to catch sentence errors in someone else's writing rather than in your own. (You are, in a sense, too close to your own work.) Exchange a piece of writing in progress with a classmate, and check each other's work for comma splices and run-on sentences.

AVOIDING RAMBLING SENTENCES

And . . . and then . . . and . . .

(fore • words) Just as you should correct any fragments, run-ons, or comma splices in your writing, you must also be careful not to use too many *and*'s or *but*'s. The result could well be a series of rambling sentences.

> **Read the paragraph below. Look and listen for sentences which ramble on and on. Correct these sentences by taking out some (but not all) of the *and*'s, *but*'s, or *so*'s. Make your changes as neatly as possible above each sentence which needs correcting. Also, correct or add punctuation and capitalization as needed. (See "Rambling sentences" in your handbook index for help.)**

After being flicked off Tom Sawyer's fingers, the pinchbug landed on its back in the aisle of the church. Tom's sore finger immediately went into his mouth as he eyed the beetle and just then a curious poodle came up the aisle so he saw the pinchbug and started to play with it. There was a yelp, and the pinchbug went flying farther down the aisle. The poodle tried to find pleasure in chasing a fly but soon lost interest. The dog had forgotten that the pinchbug was there and he sat on it so there was another yelp and the dog went streaking up the aisle like a woolly comet. The dog then changed its course and jumped into its master's lap but the master tossed the dog out the window and the voice of the distressed dog could be heard loud and clear. After the sermon Tom Sawyer went home quite happy and he didn't mind that the dog had played with his pinchbug but he did not think that it was upright for him to carry it off.

(after • words) Write a paragraph (or short paper) about a memorable animal—perhaps a pet-related experience. Exchange first drafts with a classmate. Check each other's writing for any rambling ideas. Correct these errors when you revise your writing.

USING THE RIGHT WORD 1

Camp Runamuck

If the underlined word is incorrect, cross out the word and write the correct form above it. Do not change a word which is correct.

Example: Our ~~weak~~ *week* at Camp Runamuck was

highlighted by the appearance of a

~~heard~~ *herd* of deer and a styrofoam shark.

1. "The <u>dessert</u> hike was fun," said the counselor, "but <u>whose</u> ready for a dip in the lake?"

2. One girl <u>seamed</u> uninterested in swimming; she had no <u>flare</u> for the sport.

3. She <u>choose</u> to go to the crafts class <u>ware</u> they were going to <u>die</u> T-shirts.

4. The <u>hole</u> area lit up when the camp fires <u>flared</u>.

5. Touring the <u>capitol</u> building sounds interesting, but right now I'd rather eat <u>desert</u> at the bakery next door.

6. Gray clouds told us that rain would dampen the day sooner <u>ore</u> <u>latter</u>.

7. It is good <u>council</u> not to touch the sides of your <u>canvass</u> tent during a rainstorm.

8. The <u>continual</u> (nonstop) rain not only ruined our picnic plans, but it <u>maid</u> a sopping mess of our campground.

9. Just outside our tent, a frightened opossum <u>feigned</u> being dead, and I almost <u>feinted</u> when I stumbled over it.

10. Our week at camp ended with <u>complements</u>, good-byes, and promises to <u>wright</u> soon and often.

USING THE RIGHT WORD 2

Independence Day

(fore • words) When is it important to know if one word (good) should be used instead of another word (well)? The answer to that is easy. It's important to use the right word whenever you are going to share your thoughts in a formal or semiformal situation. For example, whenever you write a report for a science class, speak in front of a church group, or write a letter requesting information, you should use the language correctly. An informed and educated public expects it.

The series of activities that follow identify many of the pairs of words that are often misused. Make special note of the words that commonly confuse you. Also, make sure to refer to "Using the Right Word" in your handbook whenever you have a usage question. (See "Usage and commonly mixed pairs" in the index.)

▮ **If the underlined word is incorrect, cross out the word and write the correct form above it. Do not change a word which is correct.**

Example: It was a hot summer morning in 1939, but the people who lived in

and around tiny Orange City, Iowa, were ~~already~~ *all ready* to experience

the ~~perennial~~ *annual* Fourth of July celebration.

1. In the village park, <u>a</u> large <u>blew</u> <u>canon</u> lay on a frame suspended <u>between</u> two

   spoked, wooden wheels.

2. <u>Besides</u> the big gun, three huge balls rested on a square wooden <u>bass</u>.

3. Two paunchy, uniformed, World War I veterans stood on either side of the <u>cannon</u>.

   A large <u>amount</u> of inquisitive spectators had gathered around them to watch the

   traditional opening exercise.

4. The mayor, who also ran the Farmers Co-op Elevator, was just finishing his speech:

   "... and the reason we're <u>altogether</u> in this safe, free, grand country of ours is

   not simply a result of this being our place of <u>berth</u>."

5. "As <u>alot</u> of you older folks remember, when President Wilson told us to take up arms, we all willingly <u>ascented</u> and <u>excepted</u> that command."

6. "We <u>new</u> that the enemy guns and tanks and subs would <u>effect</u> deaths in our own families."

7. "And we all had a fear of this <u>pane</u> <u>alright,</u> but more importantly, we <u>knew</u> that the <u>principle</u> of our freedom was at stake!"

8. "When the call to duty came, we believed that free people <u>may</u> not (are not able) <u>be</u> free to stand <u>buy</u> and watch others <u>brake</u> up their democracy!"

9. The mayor unhooked his thumbs from the suspenders of his overalls and stabbed his large right hand into the air to emphasize his last point: "So our soldier boys <u>brought</u> their guns and bullets over to the other side of the ocean, so they could <u>take</u> back a new lease on freedom to this side of the ocean!"

10. The crowd, comprised of farmers in striped suspender pants, housewives in freshly ironed aprons, a <u>number</u> of storekeepers, and <u>alot</u> of children, had never seemed <u>board</u> during the speech.

11. And now, <u>altogether,</u> they cheered the mayor who gave the speech; and they cheered the paunchy, round-shouldered veteran who lit the fuse; and they cheered the <u>blew</u> smoke that spat out the muzzle of the huge, old <u>cannon.</u>

12. But most of all, they cheered the <u>allusion</u> (false notion) that each one of them (women and children alike) had just fired the gun which silenced the enemy and ended the war.

(after • words) In a note to a friend, write about a recent incident or event that frustrated (or delighted) you. Then, write about this same incident in a note to a different audience—perhaps to a teacher or a parent. Circle words that you used in the note to your friend that you *didn't* use in your second note. (Share your results.)

USING THE RIGHT WORD 3

Words of Wisdom

▌ If the underlined word is incorrect, cross out the word and write the correct form above it. Do not change a word which is correct.

> *heard*
> **Example:** Haven't we all ~~herd~~ valuable words
>
> of wisdom from our elders like
>
> "Work hard" and "Plan ahead"?

1. <u>Lay</u> in bed <u>to</u> long at the beginning of the day and the <u>less</u> things you'll accomplish <u>bye</u> day's end.

2. Don't rely on someone else to say, "<u>Leave</u> me do that for you." Do for your- self; you'll be much <u>farther</u> along.

3. If you put all of <u>you're</u> eggs in one basket, then make sure that you don't <u>lose</u> that basket.

4. I've <u>scene</u> it all—from the Great Depression when you couldn't <u>by</u> a job to the postwar economic boom when men looked <u>past</u> some jobs in favor of others.

5. Keep <u>you're</u> own house in order, and you'll get along <u>good</u> with others.

6. <u>Its</u> always a good idea to respect the <u>rites</u> of your neighbors. Treat them <u>like</u> you want them to treat you.

7. Eating raw vegetables <u>mettled</u> with my digestion and <u>lead</u> to a stomachache.

8. I was never <u>aloud</u> to date until I was 21. My father was my <u>mail</u> escort to all of the school dances.

9. Paying for things with a credit card is a nuisance . . . like <u>bringing</u> excess baggage on a trip.

USING THE RIGHT WORD 4

Put it in writing!

Correct any errors by drawing a line through the error and writing the correct form above. Do not change any word which is correct.

    Example: Do members of your family often

                  sit

                ~~set~~ down to write letters?

1. Are you sumone which enjoys communicating

    threw the mail?

2. Are you a person who's heart seams to beet

    faster when you catch the site of a letter addressed to you?

3. When your in the act of taking a letter out of the mailbox, ware do you look

    first . . . at the address, at the stamp, or at the return address?

4. Did you ever write too a friend, ask for a prompt response, and than waist

    the next three weeks eagerly awaiting a reply?

5. Is they're any weigh you can determine weather someone who tells you about

    his success is writing in a vane (conceited) attempt to impress you, or in a

    sincere attempt to share a bit of his sole?

6. Some people enjoy writing letters so much that they'll steel time out of a busy

    day and write such a long letter that it exceeds the postal wait limits.

7. A letter witch exceeds the weight limit will have too have extra postage.

8. If a letter you've written seams heavy, it might be a good idea to have the post

    office way it.

9. The next time you might want to use lighter stationery and not waist any space;

    than it won't cost so much.

USING THE RIGHT WORD—REVIEW 1

. . . a dear little nuisance . . .

▌ Correct any errors by drawing a line through the error and writing the correct form above. Do not change any word which is correct.

Example: I was happy about the ~~berth~~ *birth* of

my ~~deer~~ *dear* little brother, at least

~~four~~ *for* a while.

1. Know one told me, of coarse, that he wood

    grow up too be a dear little nuisance.

2. It was one big pane to take care of Leon.

3. "But your such a good baby-sitter," my mom would council me.

4. "Now be sure to tell me if Leon starts braking things or digging wholes in

    the neighbor's yard again . . . or starts eating those plants."

5. The neighbors were all together (completely) amazed by my little brother.

6. One day Leon sat down as pieceful as could be rite in the middle of Mr. Ganetzke's

    garden and ate one beat leaf after another. It was quite a site.

7. He may have stripped that garden bear, but I had a flare for catching him doing

    anything wrong; and I told on him in a great hurry.

8. Its plane too me that Leon would have ascented to eating bugs if given half

    a chance, but I never did catch him doing that.

9. What was wrong with him any weigh? And why did I have to bee choosen to

    be his bodyguard?

10. It seamed to me that accept for my birthday, Christmas, and the Forth of July,

    life wasn't very fair.

USING THE RIGHT WORD—REVIEW 2

Get ready, get set (or is it sit?), go!

Correct any errors by drawing a line through the error and writing the correct form above. Do not change any word which is correct.

Example: Middle school presented me with
a ~~vary~~ *very* real problem.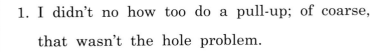

1. I didn't no how too do a pull-up; of coarse, that wasn't the hole problem.

2. I was mostly put off by all tests of physical strength and fitness; but, weather I liked it ore not, fitness tests were part of physical education, a required coarse.

3. I was to be graded on something I showed know talent four.

4. Who's fault it all was didn't matter, but I sure needed sum good council (advice) on living threw fitness tests.

5. After several vane (worthless) attempts at convincing our family doctor to right me two weeks' supply of excuses, I had to except the facts.

6. My moral (personal attitude) was low on the first mourning of the tests, but I began two feel a little better about things latter.

7. My teacher counseled (advised) me on the rite way too do a pull-up. He even gave me a complement when I razed my chin well above the bar.

8. I didn't, however, do very good on the other tests. Running gives me soar ankles, so the mile run was real hard.

9. Its a good thing we had a fire drill before the final test—push-ups.

PROOFREADING WORKSHOPS

Getting Started

Proofreading for Capitalization and Punctuation

(fore•words) Capital letters and punctuation marks are important parts of your language system. They help you keep your words and ideas under control while you write. And they help your readers enjoy the finished products you share with them. Capital letters and punctuation marks are the road markers that allow them to travel through your writing without getting lost.

While we automatically use these road markers during the writing process, we don't always use them correctly, or in the right places. That is why it is so important to proofread the final copy of your writing before you share it. You want all of the capital letters and punctuation marks to be in place, directing the flow of your ideas.

The seven **Proofreading Workshops** in this section provide a review of the common uses of capital letters, abbreviations, and punctuation marks. As you complete your work, you will learn how helpful "The Yellow Pages" in the handbook can be when you proofread. (This section is color-coded yellow.)

User's Checklist

Check your progress as you work on these **Proofreading Workshops.**

(after • words) No one expects you to know *all* of the punctuation and capitalization rules. But everyone expects you to know and follow the basic rules of mechanics. Otherwise, your writing will be too hard to follow.

CAPITALIZATION AND PUNCTUATION

Meeting Sylvia for the First Time

(fore • words) Capitalization and punctuation are the important "boundary lines" which control the movement of our writing. We *can* write without them, but, like a football or basketball game played with no "out of bounds" lines, writing in this way becomes a very confusing activity.

▌**Read the following start of a personal story written without capitalization and punctuation. You'll probably need to read it a few times to understand it.**

ill never forget the first time i saw the sylvia ann peabottom memorial library mrs delevan the librarian met our english class at the entrance and she told us to enter the library as quietly as possible as soon as she said this jerry howell bumped into sarah depies who screamed you klutz mrs delevan immediately pursed her lips she made it very clear that if we couldnt come into the library quietly we couldnt come in at all furthermore we would have to remain quiet and orderly throughout our visit or we would be asked to return to our classroom we all got the message the library was a quiet zone

▌**Now go back to the passage and put in the necessary boundary lines so that it is easier to follow. (Share your results with a classmate and with your teacher—who has the answer key.)**

(after • words) Do a 5-minute free writing on your own paper. Leave out all capital letters and punctuation marks as was done in the sample exercise. Exchange writings with a classmate to see if you can understand each other's ideas without the necessary boundary lines. Then add capital letters and punctuation marks as needed. (Refer to "Topics, Sample" in your handbook index for writing ideas.)

REVIEWING CAPS AND ABBREVIATIONS

Mrs. Goodwrench

(fore • words) **Attention to detail** means so many different things. To a car mechanic it means making sure that every wire is tightened and every new hose is securely clamped when giving an engine a tune-up. To a surgeon it means checking and double-checking to make sure that every procedure has been correctly carried out during an operation. To a chef it means testing a special sauce to make sure the right amount of seasoning has been added. To a writer it means carefully reviewing a final draft to make sure that every "i" has been dotted, every "t" has been crossed, and every capital letter has been put in place.

In this activity you will review a series of phrases or sentences to make sure that capital letters (and abbreviations) have been properly put in place. It's hard to keep track of all of the rules, especially if you haven't reviewed them in a long time, so make good use of the rules listed in your handbook. (Refer to "Capitalization" and "Abbreviations" in the index.)

Put a line through any word or letter below which is capitalized or abbreviated incorrectly. Correct each error.

An activity strategy: Go through the list once, and make the changes you are sure of. Then, for those you are not sure of, review the rules in your handbook. Still stuck? Ask a classmate or your teacher for help.

1. Home of mrs goodwrench

2. The Mayor is going to speak Tues.

3. Did you call me, uncle Jim?

4. Go East until you come to the library.

5. Isn't your Mother from the East?

6. This humid august weather is unbearable.

7. I heard mom calling for you, Dad.

8. I've always liked History Courses. Are you taking history 201 next Fall?

9. Mr. Kipp let me read <u>there's a bat in bunk five</u>.

10. Castles were quite common in the Middle ages.

11. Are you going to take that job out west?

12. the Battle of Bunker Hill

13. No, I am going to take the job down South.

14. She shouted, "don't touch the stove!"

15. a Navaho indian, Dutch pastry, Chinese muslin

16. Have you read "by the waters of babylon"?

17. The Chicago *Trib.* is a fine newspaper.

18. Bill Clinton is a democrat; he was once the governor of Arkansas.

19. "make room," barked the mover. "This piano is heavy."

20. "jerome," yelled coach rogers, "stay back on defense!"

21. They'll put men on the Planet Mars.

22. lakes Michigan and Superior

23. Mississippi and Colorado Rivers

24. the bailey middle school science club will sell refreshments.

25. Bob Madsen, m.d.

26. Mr Jackson, Marty's father, joined the staff at Trinity hospital.

27. Kellogg's crispix

28. first amendment to the constitution of the U S A

29. He's busy with his American History 212 assignment.

30. Hawaii is in the Pacific ocean.

(after • words) Here's a special challenge: supply the necessary capital letters in the following narrative. (There are 50 capital letters needed.)

america's best-loved radio program, *a prairie home companion*, left the air on june 13, 1987, at the height of its popularity. coming to you from the world theater in st. paul, minnesota, the show charmed millions of listeners. host garrison keillor took his audience into the heart and soul of an imaginary town in minnesota called lake wobegon—also known by the following title: "the town that time forgot and the decades could not improve." who will ever forget father emo, our lady of perpetual responsibility, the sidetrack tap, bertha's kitty boutique, powdermilk biscuits, ralph's pretty good grocery, and "the statue of the unknown norwegian"?

END PUNCTUATION REVIEW

Give me a question mark and a period . . . to go.

(fore • words) Punctuation, along with capitalization, controls the movement of your writing. The end punctuation marks—periods, question marks, exclamation points—signal the end of a sentence. The comma signals a break or pause in a sentence. Considering these two simple points, punctuation—especially end punctuation—is not a difficult part of writing.

> **Place periods, question marks, and exclamation points where they are needed in the following narrative. Also, supply the necessary capital letters. (Refer to "Punctuation, marking" in your handbook index for rules and examples.)**

since we had pulled in late the night before, we had no idea where our tent was pitched we knew only what stood within the dome of light cast by our Coleman lantern

as soon as the birds began to twitter, my little brother and I were up the others were still tossing in their clammy sleeping bags when we unzipped the door we squeezed through and jumped to our feet we couldn't wait to get going

to our surprise, we stood about 100 yards from a lake how green it was, even in the morning haze at the shore, we picked up rocks and heaved them wherever they landed, large dark circles opened up, then closed again the lake was covered with a thick blanket of algae

the silence of the morning was broken only by the calls of birds, the dripping of the trees, and the ploops made by our high-arching stones suddenly we heard a tremendous splash along the shore we wheeled around "look at that " my brother shouted algae was splattered over a 20-foot circle and ripples were spreading fast

"no fish could have done that," i said

"maybe a big turtle " my brother shouted

"or somebody threw a log," I said "except nobody else is here "

"could it be a sea serpent " my brother whispered

"there are no such things," i counseled him

"oh no then what is that " he pointed to a line of humps moving in the water far across the lake i saw them, too they moved, then disappeared, then reappeared, and then swam out of sight

i wanted to believe in creatures like the loch ness monster why not my little brother believed with all his heart but i felt too old for that i thought about schools of fish, diving birds, wheels falling from airplanes, meteors from outer space—scientific sorts of things

what made the splash i'll never know the dome of light around me has widened as I've grown older but i'm still not sure exactly where our tent was pitched

(after • words) Write a journal entry (or a first draft) about a mysterious, scary, or stirring experience. Don't hold back. Let your reader share in the mystery and excitement of this time.

Note: Start your story right in the middle of the action. "Once upon a time" beginnings are not allowed.

USING COMMAS

That's a lot of commas!

(fore • words) Of all of the punctuation marks, the one that has the most uses (and probably causes the most confusion) is the comma. You will note that your handbook devotes 15 topic numbers to the different rules for using commas. Do we (the handbook editors and your teachers) expect you to memorize all of these rules? No . . . but we would like you to become familiar with as many of them as you can. That's why we've designed this activity. Read on, and become better acquainted with commas.

■ Review the comma rules in your handbook, and then fill in the blanks below. Place commas correctly in each sample sentence.

1. Commas are used between words, phrases, or clauses in a _____ .

   My favorite foods are pizza hamburgers and french fries.

2. Commas are used to separate the digits in a _____ in order to distinguish hundreds, thousands, millions, etc.

   My mother must have told me at least 1 0 0 0 0 0 0 times to improve

   my diet.

3, Use commas to distinguish items in an _____ and items in a

   _____ .

   On February 1 2000 we will be moving to Boston Massachusetts.

4. Commas are used to set off the _____ _____ of the speaker from the rest of the sentence.

   " I'm sure " said Dad in a reassuring tone " that Boston has some good

   pizza parlors."

5. A comma separates an _____ or weak exclamation from the rest of the sentence.

   Yes we'll be there on time.

6. Commas are used to set off a word, phrase, or clause that _____ the main thought of a sentence.

   We can't however stay very long.

7. Use a comma to separate a noun of _____ _____ from the rest of the sentence.

   Dad is that all you think I'm worried about?

8. Commas are used to enclose a title, _____, or _____ which follow a person's last name.

   G. L. Martin M. D. and McDougal Samuel T. are rushing to the golf course.

9. A comma may be used between two _____ _____ which are joined by coordinate conjunctions.

   The two friends love to go golfing and they are working to qualify for the state tournament next year.

10. A comma should separate an _____ clause or a long

    _____ phrase from the independent clause which follows it.

    After practicing many long hours they should certainly qualify.
    (long modifying phrase)

    When they were practicing the rest of the class remained quiet. (clause)

11. Commas are used to separate two or more _____ which equally modify the same noun.

    My uncle beamed as he took hold of the large shining trophy.

12. Commas should separate an _____ phrase (or appositive) from the rest of the sentence.

    My uncle an expert angler won top prize in the fishing contest. (appositive)

13. Commas are used to punctuate _____ phrases and clauses (those which are not necessary to the basic _____ of the sentence).

Uncle Josh who had traveled 600 miles to participate was very glad he had entered the fishing contest.

14. Commas should _____ be placed around restrictive phrases and clauses (those which are needed for the clear meaning of the sentence).

The man who won the fishing contest was very glad he had entered.

Practice Using Commas

After reviewing the comma rules in the previous exercise, place commas correctly in the following sentences.

1. A group of geese is a *gaggle* but it is more commonly called a *flock*.
2. A *clip joint* is a shop store bar or other place of business where customers are overcharged.
3. Acrophobia is the fear of heights claustrophobia is the fear of enclosed spaces and hydrophobia is the fear of water.
4. Abraham Lincoln was born on February 12 1809 on a farm near Hodgenville Kentucky.
5. Mr. Lincoln served as president of the United States from March 4 1861 to April 15 1865.
6. On June 3 1979 6 0 0 0 0 0 0 tons of oil spilled from an oil well in the Gulf of Mexico.
7. Mark's new address is 310 Greens Drive Boston Massachusetts.
8. Send your requests to the *Daily Post* 211 Main Street Willowlane Missouri.
9. "Did you know" asked Dan "that London Bridge is no longer in London?"
10. Sue these are my parents.
11. Mr. Dobson our English teacher is out with the flu.
12. Sliding into first base I scraped my elbow raw.

(after • words) Come up with three sentences which are confusing without commas. Here's an example: (Share your results.)

While cleaning my brother accidentally smashed a mirror.
(A comma is really needed after "cleaning.")

PUNCTUATING DIALOGUE

Look who's talking!

(fore • words) Talking sure is easy. It's so easy that we don't have to think about it. We just . . . talk. As most of you know, recording "talk" on paper is not so free and easy. It can actually be a lot of work, especially when it comes to punctuating the specific words we say. There are a number of definite rules to follow regarding the use of quotation marks, commas, end marks, and capital letters. This activity will give you a chance to review the rules for punctuating dialogue (written conversation) and then apply what you've learned.

▐ **Punctuate the following sentences with quotation marks, commas, and end marks. Make sure to review the rules in your handbook for punctuating dialogue before you work on these sentences.**

Note: When the words of a speaker are interrupted, punctuate the sentences in the following ways:

"My sweet tooth is acting up," said Mark. "How about going for some ice cream?"
(A period is placed after "Mark" to signal the end of one sentence.)

"Yum," said Rose, "and this was going to be the first day of my diet."
(A comma is placed after "Rose" because the second part of the dialogue continues what was started before the interruption.)

1. I'm tired said Mr. Baxter Let's close early

2. That's a great idea exclaimed Lisa

3. Look out behind you yelled Trevor

4. Did you hear someone yell Look out behind you asked Lisa

5. Everyone stop where you are and get your hands up barked the masked man

   This is a stickup

6. Oh my gosh whined Sarah flatly it's a real live stickup Oh dear Just let me

   get my coat

(after • words) Re-create a phone conversation (or make one up) between you and a friend or parent or . . . Make the conversation as realistic as possible. (Check the punctuation carefully before you share the finished product with your classmates.)

USING OTHER FORMS OF PUNCTUATION

A Real Mixed Bag

(fore • words) If you look at the chart of punctuation marks in your handbook, you'll see that there are many marks available to writers—far more than you'll ever have to worry about. But there are a few punctuation marks in that chart—other than periods, commas, question marks, etc.—that you should become familiar with. Read on and see what marks we're referring to. (Work on "A Real Mixed Bag" with a partner if your teacher allows it.)

■ Review the rules in your handbook about using *semicolons* and *colons*. Then punctuate the following sentences correctly. (The first one is done for you.)

1. LuAnn is my sister; Karen is her friend.

2. I'd like everyone in their places by 7:30 a.m. however, don't break any speed limits getting here.

3. Say these words over and over to yourself I can do it, I can do it.

4. Don't forget the items on that list sleeping bag, canteen, towel, soap, and toothbrush.

5. I've decided against the triple-fudge, double-decker special I'm having a single-dip vanilla cone instead.

6. My grandmother has lived in Hawaii for five years as a result, she doesn't like to visit the Midwest during winter.

7. Martin Luther King began his famous freedom speech with these words "I have a dream."

8. Our flight stopped in Denver, Colorado Salt Lake City, Utah and San Antonio, Texas.

■ Review the rules in your handbook about using *hyphens* and *dashes*. Then punctuate the following sentences correctly. (The first one is done for you.)

1. That's not your run-of-the-mill slam dunk.

2. Your brother in law really knows how to build cars.

3. My great grandfather is ninety nine today.

4. There's only one sport I've ever enjoyed swimming.

5. Make a U turn so we can go back to that gas station.

6. No one and I mean no one may leave this room.

7. The puppy skidded on the ice covered sidewalk.

8. Arlo Hale is the president elect of the Nottingham Running Club

■ Indicate whether each of the underlined words uses an apostrophe correctly (C) or incorrectly (I). (See your handbook for rules concerning the apostrophe.)

Paula Doughty loves to ride her <u>friend's</u> unicycle; she rides it with so much skill her friend has made her part owner of the vehicle. A unicycle is recognized easily by <u>it's</u> one wheel. <u>Paula's</u> friend received the unicycle from his bother-in-law; <u>its</u> seat is mounted on a pole twenty feet high. Naturally, the <u>unicycles'</u> pedals must be up near the seat. Their vehicle is not your usual, run-of-the-mill unicycle. Because <u>it's</u> hard, sweaty work pumping a unicycle from twenty feet up, <u>it's</u> equipped with <u>it's</u> own fan. The fan is installed on the twenty-foot pole; a generator is attached to the <u>wheel's</u> hub. <u>Paula's</u> and her <u>friend's</u> riding machine is a sight to see. Now they can't wait to see the <u>brother's-in-law</u> new miniature unicycle.

(after • words) Write a journal entry (or a first draft) about a "special" vehicle in your life. Make sure that you use apostrophes correctly in your writing. (Share your results.)

PUNCTUATION REVIEW

A Whale of a Problem

Proofread the paragraphs below. Draw a line through any mark of punctuation or capital letter which is used incorrectly; add any needed punctuation or capital letters. (Refer to your handbook for help.)

1   Picture a new England beach in autumn.

2 The sky is clear the sun warms your face, and

3 the green sea has washed ashore almost 100 of

4 it's most magnificent creatures to die. A biologist walks among the bloat-

5 ing bodies of the whales and he is clearly puzzled.

6   Mass whale suicides, or "strandings" as they are called, occur year

7 after year. Many men have tried to understand these unusual suicides,

8 even Aristotle the Ancient Greek, philosopher thought about the whales

9 deaths. Although he decided the whales may indeed be killing themselves

10 modern biologists are not so easily convinced."

11   One researcher points out that the whales are descended from land

12 dwelling animals. He thinks the whales may simply be "remembering"

13 their ancient roots, and beaching themselves to "go home." This habit

14 however would have put the whale close to extinction years ago the idea

15 must be dismissed.

16   A newer theory suggests that the whales blindly follow their food

17 supplies, into shallow water. For example they may swim after a shoal of

18 squid quickly eat their dinner and then find themselves too close to the

19 shore for comfort.

20   Another theory says that whales follow the earths magnetic forces

21   As though they were following a road map the whales travel wherever

22   these forces lead. Unfortunately, the magnetic flow will sometimes

23   intersect the shore and guide the whales along a collision course with

24   the beach.

25   Biologists realize of course that none of these findings are com-

26   plete — explanations. They feel that the strandings must have a num-

27   ber of causes, not just one.

(after • words) Compare your work with a classmate's before you turn it in. Share any questions you have. Discuss any differences. And make sure to double-check your work by reviewing the punctuation rules and examples in your handbook. Also, in the space above, write freely for 3 to 5 minutes about punctuating writing. Consider what's easy or hard about it, what's important or confusing.

PART III
Language and Learning Workshops

LANGUAGE WORKSHOPS

Getting Started

Words in Action

(fore•words) The **Language Workshops** look at words in action. Said in another way, the workshops look at the "grammar" of our language, the different roles words play or the parts of speech they become when they are put to use.

Now don't worry . . . we don't expect you to become expert grammarians. (But if that happens, great!) We have two other goals in mind. First, we want you to understand and appreciate more fully the standard use of our language. By standard use, we mean the language you would use in a classroom report or speech. Second, we want you to come to know the words generally used to describe our language in action. (We also want you to have some fun in the process—as you will soon see by the titles, illustrations, and nature of each workshop.)

Special Note: "The Yellow Pages" in your handbook is your complete grammar, usage, and mechanics guide. How do you find this section? Look for the pages that are . . . yellow.

User's Checklist

Check your progress as you work on these **Language Workshops.**

☐ **Identifying Nouns** • *Go figure!*

☐ **Using Specific Nouns** • *Making It Clear*

☐ **The Simple Tenses of Verbs** • *What time is it?*

☐ **The "Perfect" Tenses of Verbs** • *Take your time!*

☐ **Irregular Verbs** • *How irregular are you?*

☐ **Subject-Verb Agreement** • *Compounding the Problem*

☐ **Identifying Adjectives** • *Typecasting*

☐ **Identifying and Using Adjectives** • *Paragraph Stuffing*

☐ **Identifying Adverbs** • *Mixed Bag of Tricks*

☐ **Pronouns and Antecedents** • *I'm in favor of pronouns!*

☐ **Pronouns and Antecedents** • *Running on Empty*

☐ **Identifying Prepositions** • *He's going through one of his "phrases."*

☐ **Subordinate Conjunctions** • *I don't believe it!*

☐ **Identifying Interjections** • *May I interject this . . . ?*

☐ **Parts of Speech Review** • *"We're all in our places with bright, shiny faces."*

(after • words) Make good use of what you have learned in the workshops. How so? For one thing, when you review a classmate's writing, refer to the use of specific nouns or vivid verbs, identify agreement problems, and make note of well-placed adjectives and adverbs.

IDENTIFYING NOUNS

Go figure!

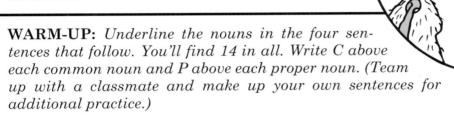

(fore • words) Here's some common "knoun-ledge." A noun names a person, a place, a thing, or an idea. If you don't believe me, check your handbook.

WARM-UP: *Underline the nouns in the four sentences that follow. You'll find 14 in all. Write C above each common noun and P above each proper noun. (Team up with a classmate and make up your own sentences for additional practice.)*

❑ All of the words in our language have been put into eight groups. (3)

❑ No, they're not called the Rolling Stones or Miami Sound Machine. (2)

❑ These groups are called the eight parts of speech. (3)

❑ Nouns and verbs are as important to our language as Mick Jagger and Gloria Estefan

are to their musical groups. (6)

_____

_____

_____

■ **Study the two lists of nouns which follow. Then add three nouns to each list. (Make sure your nouns fit with the rest of the words in each list.)**

time	clock
envy	Popsicle
love	sign
jealousy	guitar
competition	pencil
sincerity	book

_____   _____

_____   _____

_____   _____

■ **On the lines provided below explain the difference between the nouns in the two columns:**

_____

_____

_____

_____

(Share your explanation with one of your classmates. Then, compare it with the explanations in the handbook under "Concrete Noun" and "Abstract Noun." How close does your explanation match the one in the handbook?)

(after • words) Select one noun from the first list (*time* through *sincerity*) and help us "see" this word in a concrete poem, a title-down poem, or in a story. (See your handbook for help.) *Note:* Use the space above for your final poem or story.

USING SPECIFIC NOUNS

Making It Clear

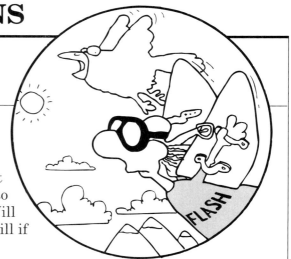

(fore • words) Would you rather watch a TV show in living color or in black and white? How about this one: Would you rather read something in full color or in black and white? If you're like most of us, your answer will be the same. You want to watch TV shows and read books in living color. Will readers "see" *your* writing in living color? They will if you use specific nouns, verbs, and modifiers.

Specific nouns are especially helpful when you are trying to create a clear image or word picture for a reader. Note the difference between the following two sentences. The first sentence contains general nouns, and it doesn't express a very clear idea. The second sentence, which includes more specific nouns, does express a clear idea.

The *pilot* entered his *plane* in the *contest*. (**general** nouns)

Ralphy entered *Flash* in the *air show*. (**specific** nouns)

Perhaps you can better understand the difference between *general* and *specific* words by looking at the examples below. (Notice that the nouns move from very general at the top to very specific at the bottom. By using a good number of specific nouns in your writing, you will make it easier for the reader to understand exactly what you are saying.)
Examples:

person	place	thing	idea
man	*building*	*book*	*impression*
artist	*arena*	*reference book*	*inspiration*
Vincent van Gogh	*Madison Square Garden*	*Farmer's Almanac*	*insight*

Now think of three nouns for each of the categories below. Each noun you add must be more specific than the one before as in the examples above.

person	place	thing	idea

Revise each of the following sentences twice. Create a clearer picture for each bold-faced word by substituting a more specific noun. Try to make sentence B even more specific than sentence A. See the example below. (You may add or change other words as necessary to create a better sentence.)

Example: The **car** drove past the **building**.

A. *The foreign car roared past the government building.*

B. *The Toyota roared past the White House.*

1. The **animal** is in the **building**.

   A. _____

   B. _____

2. The **doctor** performed the **operation**.

   A. _____

   B. _____

3. The **singer** was given an **award**.

   A. _____

   B. _____

4. A **relative** came down with an **illness**.

   A. _____

   B. _____

5. The **worker** picked up the heavy **object**.

   A. _____

   B. _____

6. The **athlete** participated in the **event**.

   A. _____

   B. _____

(after • words) Pick any four of the nouns from the example lists (at the beginning of this activity), and write them in the spaces here:

_____   _____   _____   _____

On your own paper, put all of these in one sentence. Then, put these words in a second and third sentence. For a special challenge, see how many sentences you can make. Make a contest out of this activity among your classmates.

THE SIMPLE TENSES OF VERBS

What time is it?

(fore • words) In addition to expressing an action or linking the subject to another word in a sentence, a verb expresses tense or time. The three simple tenses are the present, past, and future.

Underline the verb twice in each of the following sentences. Then put each sentence in a different "time zone." That is, rewrite each sentence so the verb is in all three simple tenses. Underline the verbs with two lines in your new sentences.

EXAMPLE:

Present: *John <u>comes</u> toward me, the visor of his baseball cap pointing sideways.*

Past: *John <u>came</u> toward me, the visor of his baseball cap pointing sideways.*

Future: *John <u>will come</u> toward me, the visor of his baseball cap pointing sideways.*

1. **Present:** *I lock the keys in the car like a dizzy-wiz.*

   Past: _____

   _____

   Future: _____

   _____

2. **Present:** _____

   _____

   Past: *I called the folks at the AAA auto club to help me.*

   Future: _____

   _____

3. **Present:** _____

_____

Past: _____

_____

Future: _In four seconds flat, the man from AAA will open my car._

4. **Present**: _"Elizabeth, what is the best way to exterminate mosquitoes?"_

Past: _____

_____

Future: _____

_____

5. **Present**: _____

_____

Past: _"With a shotgun,"_ she replied absently.

Future: _____

_____

6. **Present:** _____

_____

Past: _____

_____

Future: _The class will laugh uproariously._

(after • words) Rewrite the first paragraph in the model paper found in your handbook under the chapter "Writing About Experiences." Put all the main verbs in the present tense. Start your paragraph this way: _Here I stand . . ._

THE "PERFECT" TENSES

Take your time!

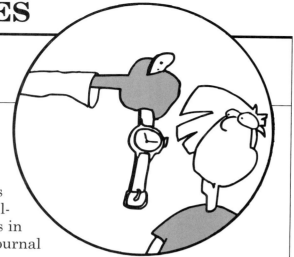

(fore • words) So much of daily life is dictated by time. We wake up to an alarm clock, move from class to class according to school time, and plan the rest of our day around supper time and prime time. By the same token, our communication is dictated by time. We relive our past in personal-experience papers; we share our present concerns in class discussions; and we look to the future in our journal and diary writing.

At times, the action you want to express isn't clearly a present, past, or future action. For example, let's say you started cleaning your locker five days ago, and you are still cleaning it. Your cleaning is neither a past action nor a present action. Instead, it is an ongoing action. When you have this type of situation, you need to use one of the three perfect tenses to state the action. Note the use of the perfect tenses in the following sentences. The verb in each sentence is in italics. (See 758-760 for more examples.)

> **Present Perfect Tense:** The amusement park always *has remained* one of my favorite places to spend a summer day.
>
> **Past Perfect Tense:** Before this year, the Monster ride *had frightened* me.
>
> **Future Perfect Tense:** After this summer, I *will have attended* the park for six straight years.

■ **Using your handbook, answer the following questions about the perfect tenses.**

1. The *present perfect* tense expresses action which began in the past but continues

   _____

   _____

2. The *past perfect* tense expresses action which began in the past and

   _____

   _____

3. The *future perfect* tense expresses action or existence which will begin in the future and

   _____

   _____

■ Underline the verb twice in each of these sentences. Don't forget to underline auxiliary verbs as well. In the space provided tell whether each verb is *present perfect*, *past perfect*, or *future perfect*. (The first one is done for you.)

Present Perfect   1. Ned Fraphoob, the ruler of the planet, has escaped in his hovercraft.

_____ 2. An earthquake had leveled the hot-dog stand.

_____ 3. He will have spent the stolen money before nightfall.

_____ 4. I have lived in an apple tree for six years.

_____ 5. In those six years, I never have seen a doctor.

■ Underline the verb twice in each of the following sentences. Then rewrite each sentence by changing the verb from a simple tense to the perfect tense indicated in parentheses. Remember that all perfect tenses are composed of a form of *have* plus the past participle of the main verb. (The first one has been done for you.)

1. The Phantom Blur prepares very carefully for the mission. *(present perfect)*

   The Phantom Blur has prepared very carefully for the mission.

2. He disguises himself cleverly. *(present perfect)*

   _____

3. He sneaks into carefully guarded embassies, castles, and prisons. *(present perfect)*

   _____

   _____

4. Tomorrow, the Phantom Blur will attempt a new mission. *(future perfect)*

   _____

5. At first, he considered the mission a pushover. *(past perfect)*

   _____

6. Perhaps tomorrow at the castle he will change his mind. *(future perfect)*

   _____

(after • words) If you're an adventurous spirit, create Phantom's next mission in a story. (See "Story writing" in your handbook index for help.)

IRREGULAR VERBS

How irregular are you?

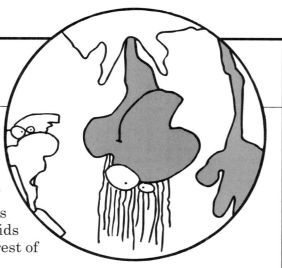

(fore • words) Irregular verbs have minds of their own. They refuse to fit into any regular pattern. How so? While the principal parts of most verbs are simply created by adding "ed" to the main verb (like, liked, has liked), the different parts of irregular verbs follow no set pattern (run, ran, has run; bite, bit, has bitten). Irregular verbs are like kids who wear striped or polka-dotted socks while the rest of the class wear only solid-colored socks.

A good way to learn these irregular verbs is simply to say them over to yourself several times. They have a certain rhythm that helps to make them stick in your mind. Try these easier ones first. Look at them and say them to yourself several times.

begin	began	begun
bite	bit	bitten
drink	drank	drunk
see	saw	seen
write	wrote	written

Of course, there are many more troublesome verbs, including the following:

bring	brought	brought
burst	burst	burst
drown	drowned	drowned
swing	swung	swung
wake	woke	waked

Use the blanks below to list any additional irregular verbs and their principal parts that you know.

_____   _____   _____

_____   _____   _____

_____   _____   _____

_____   _____   _____

Now turn to the complete chart of irregular verbs in your handbook. Read the chart carefully. Read it slowly to yourself. Listen as a classmate reads it to you. Make note of the verbs that cause you trouble. Study those. Then close your book and fill in the chart that follows. Good luck! (Check your work upon completion.)

Present Tense	Past Tense	Past Participle
am, be		
	bit	
	brought	
choose	chose	
come	came	
	did	
drag	dragged	
draw		
fall		
fight		
fly		
		known
lie (recline)		
set		
		shaken
	swam	

(after • words) Use the most troublesome verbs (from the list above) in a paragraph. Here's a possible starting point:

I brought a water balloon to the bus stop, and it . . .

SUBJECT-VERB AGREEMENT

Compounding the Problem

(fore • words) All of the individual parts in our sentences have to **agree**; otherwise, our writing will be confusing. For example, if some of the *ideas* in our sentences don't necessarily agree, we might end up with crazy thoughts like the following ones: (These sentences come from *Anguished English* by Richard Lederer.)

Milwaukee is the golden egg that the rest of the state wants to milk.
(Are we talking chickens, cows, or a new animal I'm not aware of?)

Don't sit there like a sore thumb!
(Hmm, whatever happened to sticking out like a sore thumb or sitting there like a bump on a log?)

This activity reviews a far more common type of "agreement problem" called **subject-verb agreement**. All language arts teachers remind student writers that the subjects and verbs in their sentences must agree in number, so we know that you have heard of this problem.

You remember the rules, right? Singular subjects must agree in number with singular verbs (*Roscoe eats*), and plural subjects must agree in number with plural verbs (*Roscoe and Garfield eat*). Pay special attention to the second part of this review activity. It discusses some special subject-verb agreement problems.

WARM-UP: *In the following sentences, underline the subject with one line and the verb with two lines. Also correct any subject-verb agreement errors. (Check your answers against those of a classmate.)*

1. Our family <u>dog</u> Roscoe <u>eats</u> nothing but human food.

2. He love family leftovers.

3. One of his favorite dishes is macaroni and cheese.

4. Sometimes, he only eat peanut butter sandwiches.

5. He even has a taste for hot food.

6. Most dogs in our neighborhood gets dry dog food.

7. Roscoe just about gag at the sight of a bag of Purina Dog Chow.

8. By the way, Roscoe is not a small dog.

Can I come to some "agreement"?

Read through the following three sets of sentences. Then, carefully read through the subject/verb agreement rules in your handbook. Afterward, label each set of sentences according to the correct rule. (Use the topic number and subtitle for your label.)

Topic Number: _____   Subtitle: _____

Ketchup and mustard make scrambled eggs taste like hamburgers.

Neither my sister nor her friends believe that ghosts exist.

Coke or Pepsi is fine for me.

Topic Number: _____   Subtitle: _____

The basketball squad is a source of pride for the school.

Her family buy their shoes at separate stores.

Your rock group needs more space to hold its practice.

Topic Number: _____   Subtitle: _____

Each of these cars has a defect.

Half of the artists were surprised at the contest winners.

Half of the pie was eaten by noon.

(after • words) Write five sentences with the following words or word groups as the subjects: *the coach or her players, anybody, mathematics, most,* and *Leroy and his classmates.* When you're done, exchange papers with a classmate, and check each other's work using the subject/verb agreement rules in your handbook as a guide.

IDENTIFYING ADJECTIVES

Typecasting

(fore • words) Will studying nouns, verbs, adjectives, and other parts of speech make you a better writer? No, it won't. But it will make it easier for you to talk about writing. It's much easier and more exact to say, "Use specific nouns and adjectives," than it is to say, "Use specific naming words and modifiers."

Let's see how good you are at typecasting the following adjectives. No, these words aren't auditioning for a new TV series. They've already earned their parts. What we really want you to do is identify the role each of the underlined adjectives plays in the following sentences.

> **Each sentence has a different type of adjective underlined. In the space beneath each blank, provide an explanation for each type. You'll find help in your handbook index under "Adjective, Types."**

1. <u>Some</u> cats enjoy having <u>many</u> mice around.

   Type: _____

   Explanation: An _____ adjective is one which _____

   _____

2. <u>This</u> kitten is mean, but <u>that</u> cat is meaner.

   Type: _____

   Explanation: _____

   _____

3. <u>Scar-faced</u> Bronty is no <u>scaredy-cat</u> guard.

   Type: _____

   Explanation: _____

   _____

4. A frustrated kitten is <u>unpleasant</u>.

Type: _____

Explanation: _____

_____

I'm not sure.

Use one of the four types of adjectives as one of the central characters in a story. An *indefinite adjective*, for example, might only think or speak in very general terms. Its favorite phrase might be "Gee, I'm not sure." A *demonstrative adjective*, on the other hand, might be very bossy. (Ask your teacher if you may work in pairs for this activity.)

(after • words) Share your stories in your writing groups or with your class as a whole. Pay special attention to the adjective's personality.

IDENTIFYING AND USING ADJECTIVES

Paragraph Stuffing

(fore • words) You can't possibly learn all there is to know about writing and speaking by merely writing and speaking. You must also read like a writer, taking note of how other people express themselves in print. And the same holds true for speaking. Listen carefully to how other people use words in speeches. Some of the things you pick up on will eventually work their way into your own communicating.

WARM-UP: *On the lines provided below, copy the first two sentences in the introduction to "Group Advising" in your hand-book. ("All writers like . . . .") Underline the adjectives after you copy them. You'll find seven. Do not count* a, an, *or* the. *(See "Adjective" in your handbook for help.)*

1. _____

_____

2. _____

_____

■ **On your own paper, stuff as many adjectives as you can into a paragraph.** (***My fluffy, overstuffed, king-of-the-house* cat . . .**)

■ **After you finish your paragraph, exchange your work with a partner and see who is the best stuffer. That is, see who used the most adjectives. Do not count** *a, an,* **or** *the***.**

(after • words) Rewrite your partner's paragraph using adjectives more selectively. Writing that is overflowing with adjectives sounds unnatural. Share your results.

IDENTIFYING ADVERBS

Mixed Bag of Tricks

(fore • words) Here are two more bloopers from *Anguished English* for you to enjoy. (The italicized adverbs in these crazy ads help create the humor.)

Toaster: A gift that every member of the family appreciates. *Automatically* burns toast.

Auto Repair Service: Try us once and you'll *never* go anywhere else.

Lightning Strikes!

▌ **Underline the nine adverbs in the following sentences. (If you're not sure what an adverb is, look in your handbook.)**

Lightning streaked continuously, driving jagged spears into the dark night.

John's mother hesitantly and shakily agreed that the lightning was pretty.

Four-year-old John found the whole experience quite exciting.

Suddenly, they were plunged into darkness.

To move in the dark was very difficult, but they slowly managed to find their way.

They walked cautiously across the busy intersection.

John and his mother will never forget that experience.

(after • words) Read "An Invitation to Writing" (004-005) and find at least six adverbs. No, make that five adverbs. We'll list one for you. (Share your results.)

___*especially*___   _____   _____

_____   _____   _____

PRONOUNS AND ANTECEDENTS

I'm in favor of pronouns!

(fore • words) Which general meaning of the prefix *pro* helps define pronoun—"forward" or "in favor of"? If you answered, "In favor of," you're right, because a pronoun is used in favor of (or in place of) a noun.

▌Use the sentence that follows as the starting point for a short paragraph (four or five sentences). Be sure to identify who the someone is before your writing comes to a close.

There's someone at the door. _____

_____

_____

_____

_____

_____

_____

_____

Special Note: Consider *when* the visitor came to the door, *what* door he or she came to, and for *what* purpose.

Who's that knocking at your door?

▌Share your paragraphs in groups of two or three, and see who came to each other's door. The name (or word) that identifies the visitor is called an antecedent. Refer to your handbook for a definition of *antecedent*, and write it in the space provided below.

_____

_____

(after • words) Now that you know what an antecedent is, think how your paragraph would read without it. Your sentences wouldn't be very clear, would they?

SPECIAL CHALLENGE ACTIVITY
PRONOUNS AND ANTECEDENTS

Running on Empty

(fore • words) You should always write so your reader has a clear understanding of what it is you're trying to say. The writers of the following sentences obviously weren't careful or clear in what they said. Read and enjoy. (Taken from *Anguished English* by Richard Lederer.)

❑ About two years ago, a wart appeared on my left hand, which I wanted removed.

❑ It is bad manners to break your bread and roll in your soup.

❑ When Lincoln was president, he wore only a tall silk hat. (Think about it!)

Make sure that the antecedent of a pronoun (the word the pronoun refers to) is always clear in your writing. Otherwise, you will end up with a sentence like the following one:

Unclear Pronoun Use:

I took my car to the corner gas station because it was nearly empty.

(This sentence does not clearly state *what* was nearly empty—the car or the gas station—because the antecedent of the pronoun *it* is unclear.)

This idea could be more clearly stated as follows:

Clear Pronoun and Antecedent:

Because my car was nearly empty, I took it to the corner gas station.

(*Car* is definitely the antecedent of the pronoun *it* in this sentence.)

Rewrite each of the following sentences so that the pronoun has a clearly stated antecedent. Refer to the examples above for help. (Se sure to use the italicized pronoun in your new sentences.)

1. Reggie sat in the first row of the theater since *it* was empty.

_____

_____

_____

2. When I put my foot into the shoe, *it* was wet.

_____

_____

_____

3. When the ice floe reached the old dam, *it* broke.

_____

_____

_____

4. After he'd left the present on the doorstep, Gerard realized *it* was the wrong one.

_____

_____

_____

5. Even though the chauffeur drove his limousine into the bicycle, *it* wasn't damaged.

_____

_____

_____

(after • words) Turn to the chart of singular and plural personal pronouns in your handbook. (Look under "Pronoun, Person" in your handbook index.) Study it carefully! Then close your book, and see how many of the pronouns you can list. You might want to do this in the form of a cluster. ("Personal pronouns" would be your nucleus phrase.) Check your list against the one in your handbook. Also, see how you did compared to your classmates.

IDENTIFYING PREPOSITIONS

He's going through one of his "phrases."

(fore • words) Our language is ever changing. We are constantly adding new words, particularly because of all of today's technological advances. We are also dropping other words that, for one reason or another, have fallen out of favor. Some of the words with the most staying power are the most common ones, the shortest ones, the ones we use time and time again. **Prepositions** are among these words. *At, about, by, for, in, of, on,* and *to,* among others, have been used in our language for well over 1,400 years.

WARM-UP: *Turn to "Selecting a Writing Subject" in your handbook. (See "Selecting, Topics" in the index.) Read the opening paragraph once for meaning (and your enjoyment). Then read it again and make note of the prepositional phrases in this piece. List them in the space provided below. (See a list of prepositions in your handbook for help. Note: "To help" and "to fool around with" are special types of verb phrases, not prepositional phrases.)*

So what?

Okay, you say, so what's the big deal about prepositional phrases? Here's our answer. Prepositional phrases are indispensable words in our language. (*Indispensable* means we can't do without them.) Just think how sentences like the following ones would read without the prepositional phrases (phrases in italics). There wouldn't be much left, would there?

Write *on a regular basis in a personal journa*l.

Begin writing *with a particular idea in mind.*

Adding Variety

Prepositional phrases can also add variety to your writing. If, for example, all of your sentences start in the same way (probably with the subject), move a prepositional phrase to the beginning of some of them. (See the example sentences.)

A pit bull terrier played the gentle Petey in the Our Gang movies.

In the Our Gang movies, *a pit bull terrier played the gentle Petey.*

(The prepositional phrase has been moved to the beginning of the second sentence.)

Rewrite the following sentences so that each begins with a prepositional phrase. Place a comma after the phrase if you think the meaning of the sentence would be unclear without this punctuation.

1. Pit bulls are often bred and trained to be fighters in this day and age.

   _____

   _____

2. Some pit bulls are vicious because of cruel treatment by their owners.

   _____

   _____

3. Some owners give them live poultry to tear apart for training.

   _____

4. The meanest pit bulls are sometimes used in illegal dogfights according to concerned pet owners.

   _____

   _____

5. Drug dealers in big cities often use pit bulls to clear other people off the sidewalk.

   _____

   _____

(after • words) Write at least one eye-catching story starter using one of the **two-word** or **phrasal prepositions** from the list in the handbook. The model that follows might help you write your own story starter. (Share your results.)

Together with *her two friends, Elisha was a curious young lady. One foggy September evening, her curiosity led to danger. She and her friends discovered an unlocked back door at the new factory at the edge of town . . .*

SUBORDINATE CONJUNCTIONS

I don't believe it!

(fore • words) You already know an incredible amount about the English language, and you have for a long time. Before you even set foot in a schoolroom, you were a good talker, right? It's with the written language (and more formal uses of speech) that you need practice. That's why your teachers give you plenty of opportunities to write, and that's why we provide you with activities like the following one. We want to help you learn as much as you can about your language.

WARM-UP: *Read through the following set of sentences. Note how the same general thought is expressed in three different ways:*

As two sentences:

> *Martha entered a 124-mile ice-skating race. She feels ready for it.*

As a compound sentence:

> *Martha entered a 124-mile ice-skating race, and she feels ready for it.*
>   (The coordinate conjunction *and* connects the two sentences.)

As a complex sentence:

> *Martha entered a 124-mile ice-skating race because she feels ready for it.*
>   (The subordinate conjunction *because* connects the two sentences.)

Discussion: Generally speaking, the more experienced you become as a writer (and reader), the more often you will use complex sentences like the last sample sentence above. Why? They often carry more meaning and make your writing read more smoothly.

The "glue" that makes them work.

Subordinate conjunctions connect or "glue" two ideas together to form meaningful complex sentences. That is their sole reason for being. Some subordinate conjunctions express time (before), some express the reason why (because), and others serve as conditional words (unless). In each of the sentences on the next page, do the following three things:

1. Circle the subordinate conjunctions. (See your handbook for a complete list.)

2. Put in parentheses the group of words (or clause) each conjunction introduces.

3. Underline the other group of words the subordinate clause is "glued" to.

Example: For his own safety, a soccer referee in Greece had to disguise himself as a priest after the match (because) he had greatly upset the local fans.)

1. Alex Wickham must have had a lot of confidence since he dove from a cliff the height of a 20-story building.

2. He lost consciousness before he hit the water.

3. Although he survived the dive, his body was all black-and-blue.

4. Two tennis players once continued a point for 78 straight minutes until one player had to stop the volley to give a tennis lesson.

5. When Lawson Robertson and Harry Hillman set a track-and-field record, they did it in a three-legged race.

6. Although he had a 150-pound man on his back, Noah Young ran a mile in 8 minutes 30 seconds.

7. So that he could weigh in at 232 pounds for a wrestling match, William Cobb lost 507 pounds in three years.

8. Johann Huslinger walked 10 hours a day on his hands before he reached Paris.

(after • words) Write a paragraph about a cooking, camping, or classroom experience in which you use your very best "Look, Dick. See Spot run" style. That is, write in short, simple sentences as if you were just learning to read and write. Then exchange paragraphs and revise each other's work so that it reflects your present style of writing. Discuss the results. (Try to use some subordinate conjunctions in your revisions.)

IDENTIFYING INTERJECTIONS

May I interject this . . . ?

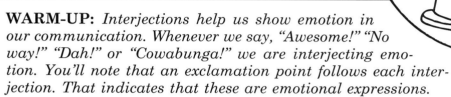

(fore • words) If you want to become a real student of your language, listen carefully to the ways a variety of people express themselves. Everyone has his or her own special way of saying certain things. Make note of expressions you find especially interesting. Many professional writers and studiers of languages carry a notepad just for this purpose.

WARM-UP: *Interjections help us show emotion in our communication. Whenever we say, "Awesome!" "No way!" "Dah!" or "Cowabunga!" we are interjecting emotion. You'll note that an exclamation point follows each interjection. That indicates that these are emotional expressions.*

    That doesn't mean that an exclamation point has to follow an interjection. If the interjection doesn't show really strong emotion, set it off from the rest of the sentence with a comma. Note the interjections at the beginning of the sentences that follow:

Cowabunga! School's canceled!

Aah, what's so good about that?

▮ **List below some of the common interjections you use in speech and in writing. (Use common sense and good taste. This is a classroom assignment.)**

(after • words) Develop a conversation, real or imagined, in which you use some of the interjections you've listed. This might be an argument or a phone conversation. It might be an extremely happy, intense, or exciting moment. (See "Dialogue, Writing" for guidelines.)

PARTS OF SPEECH REVIEW

"We're all in our places with bright, shiny faces."

(fore • words) What part of speech is the most important? In one respect that's a silly question. Obviously, they all are very important. But there is one part of speech that really does seem to serve as the core of communication. What part of speech am I talking about? Think about this as you work through the activities on this sheet. Ask your partner what he or she thinks. Then, as a class, discuss this question, and see if you can come up with an answer.

WARM-UP: *Name one of the eight parts of speech in each of the eight "bright, shiny faces." Don't look in your handbook (at least, not yet), but rather, try to name all of them on your own. Then, if the "inkwell" runs dry and you can't think of any more, refer to your handbook.*

Let's interface over parts of speech.

Pair up with a classmate and, as a team, identify the part of speech for each under-lined word. There are five examples of each part of speech, except for the interjection, which has only one example. (A few words have already been labeled for you.)

In the summer after eighth grade, Rene took a bus from Vermont to her uncle's cottage in New Jersey. Her "graduation present" turned out to be a crash course in the school of life.

At a stop in New York City, she visited a newsstand. Suddenly, someone slit her shoulder strap and stole her purse. She never saw the thief. Her ticket, her money, and all her junk were gone.

What anguish! She kept patting her side as if the bag would reappear. Anger and dread overwhelmed her. Oh, how could someone be so evil? And how would she get to Ocean City now?

Fortunately, the driver let her call her parents. They told her about Western Union, the nationwide telegraph network. They promised to wire money within an hour to the nearest agent.

Hiking through the litter of downtown Manhattan, she composed herself. In high school, she was sure, she would write a fine story about her adventure. In the grimy little Western Union office, she studied people with a writer's eye. They looked sick, strung out, and afraid. A few looked wasted by drugs. Everyone there had a problem. But when a man in a tie-dyed T-shirt said crazy things, everybody laughed. They became a kind of family.

Days later, while sunning on the Jersey shore, she thought about the crowded place. Her story would not be about crime and litter. It would be about the feelings that draw people together.

(after • words) Write sentences on your own with examples of the different parts of speech underlined. Exchange your sentences with those of a classmate.

READING AND LEARNING STRATEGIES

Taking Charge of Your Study-Reading

(fore•words) Do you find it hard to keep track of important facts and details in reading assignments? Do you jump headfirst into reading material with no plan in mind? Do you sometimes have trouble figuring out the main idea "behind" the reading? Don't worry. If you answer yes to these questions, you're not a "reading wreck." You've just become a little lazy with your reading, or perhaps you've picked up some bad reading habits. Or then again, maybe you never learned how to read factual material. In any case, this section has a number of helpful strategies that will help you take charge of your study-reading.

The nine **Reading and Learning Strategies** cover everything from reading maps to finding the main idea, from summarizing as you read to finding the order of important details. There's even an activity that will help you "read" an editorial cartoon. In short, these strategies cover reading from left to right, top to bottom.

Special Note: Refer to "Study-Reading Skills" in your handbook for more helpful guidelines and strategies.

Getting Started

User's Checklist

Check your progress as you work on these **Reading and Learning Strategies.**

☐   **Study-Reading** • *Before . . . and After*

☐   **Know-Want-Learn (KWL)** • *Wha-da-ya-know?*

☐   **Finding the Main Idea** • *5WH: Who, what, when . . . ?*

☐   **Finding the Main Idea** • *Diagramming Details*

☐   **Finding the "Sea"quence** • *First Things First*

☐   **Summarizing as You Read** • *In a Nutshell*

☐   **Reading Maps** • *What in the world . . . ?*

☐   **Reading Pictures** • *The Editorial Cartoon*

☐   **Reading Graphs** • *A picture is worth . . .*

(after • words) Make note of those strategies that work for you, those that will really help you make sense of challenging reading material. And then put them too good use. It's one thing to *learn* these strategies and quite another thing to *apply* them to specific assignments.

STUDY-READING

Before . . . and After

(fore • words) Did you know each of us thinks 50,000 thoughts per day? There's a lot in your head! AND there's room for much, much more. Even Einstein used only about 10 percent of his brain.

> Use the following *Before . . . and After* reading strategy when you are reading about a specific topic or idea for basic information. Try it out before and after you read the "Planet Profusion" page in your handbook. (Refer to "Planets" in the index.)

Before reading this new material,
I know these things about this topic.
(List at least two or three things you know
about our solar system.)

After reading this new material,
I added these thoughts to my brain.
(List at least two or three things that you learned.)

(after • words) Try writing "before . . . and after" statements the next time you read about a specific topic for basic information. You can simply divide a page in two (or draw two circles if you prefer).

KNOW–WANT–LEARN (KWL)

Wha-da-ya-know?

(fore • words) One of the best reading strategies you can use is the **KWL**. You can use KWL whenever you read, but especially when you begin a new chapter or area of study. How does KWL work? Read on and find out.

> **Turn to the "Using the Library" section in your handbook and find the explanation of "The Dewey Decimal System." Then follow the KWL directions given in the following diagram: (Complete your chart with a classmate if your teacher allows it.)**

K	W	L
List what you already **KNOW** about the topic before you begin reading. (List two or three points.)	List what you **WANT** to learn before and during the reading. (List two points before and one during the reading.)	List what you did **LEARN** after the reading. (List two or three points.)

(after • thought) Review your **L** list after the reading to discover if you have answered all of your questions in the **W** column. Also, add any new questions to the **W** list.

TIP: Use this strategy to measure what you **know** about a topic for a classroom report as well as what you **want** to discover.

(after • words) Share the results of your work with another team. For additional practice, give "Using Your Brain" the KWL treatment.

FINDING THE MAIN IDEA

5WH: Who, what, when . . . ?

(fore • words) One of the easiest ways to find the main idea in what you are reading is to ask the same questions reporters ask when they cover a news story: **who? what? when? where? why?** and **how?** This strategy is especially useful when reading about important events and people in newspapers, magazines, and textbooks.

▌ **Read the sample news story in your handbook. (Refer to "News story, writing" in the index.) Then apply the 5WH questions to the article. (Space has been provided below.)** *Note:* **You won't necessarily find answers to all of the questions in all news stories.**

1. Who (or what) is the article about? _____

_____

_____

_____

2. What happened? _____

_____

_____

_____

3. When? _____

4. Where? _____

5. Why? _____

6. How? _____

▌ **Now that you've gathered the pieces together, what (in one sentence) is the main idea of the article? (Share your results.)**

_____

_____

(after • words) Apply the 5WH questions to a short news article of your own choosing. Also, state the main idea of the article in one sentence. (Share your results.)

FINDING THE MAIN IDEA

Diagramming Details

The diagram (word picture) shown below provides an effective way to focus on the main idea of reading material. Note how one student used this diagram to focus on the main idea in the opening to "Writing Poetry" in your handbook.

Topic: _____ *What is poetry?* _____

Details About Topic

"Imaginary gardens with real toads in them" is one poet's definition.	Poetry can't be defined in a factual way.	A poem is an imaginative creation.	Poems come from real-life experiences.	Jump-roping jingles and song lyrics are poems in their own way.	Good poetry presents ideas in new and different ways.

Poetry is a creative way to write about real experiences.

(State the main idea in a sentence.)

Now you try! Your teacher may ask you to read another brief section. If not, use the opening to "Building Paragraphs" in the handbook. ("What is a paragraph?" is your topic.)

Topic: _____

Details About Topic

(State the main idea in a sentence.)

TIP: Look for details that answer who, what, when, where, why, and how, to include in your detail boxes. (The number of boxes in your diagram depends on the amount of detail in the reading material.)

(after • words) Skim through the index or slowly fan through another text and find a page of information that interests you. Determine the main idea of this page using the same diagram.

FINDING THE "SEA"QUENCE

First Things First

(fore • words) Stories are generally told in sequence. That is, they are told according to what happened first, second, third, and so on. History, biographies, and science experiments are told in sequence as well. Understanding (and remembering) the material in your textbooks often depends on finding the sequence of important ideas. This activity provides you with experience in putting "first things first" for a reading selection (or two).

▎ **Read the information in your handbook about "Planning and Writing the Essay Answer" (on the third page of "The Essay Test"). Study below how a student arranged this information into a *sequence* by listing the important details in the right order.**

> Title/Topic: *Writing an Essay Answer*

Sequence:

1.	*Read the question several times.*
2.	*Reword the question as a sentence.*
3.	*Use this sentence for a topic sentence.*
4.	*List, cluster, or gather your thoughts about this topic.*
5.	*Outline your answer.*
6.	*Write the essay.*

Now it's your turn!

▎ **Start with an easy one. Read the model phase autobiography entitled "Fashionation." Find the important sequence of events in this phase of the student's life and list them in order. (Use the model above as your guide.)**

(after • words) By now you should be ready for a real challenge. Read the poem "Stopping by Woods on a Snowy Evening" which you will find in the "Writing Poetry" section of your handbook. Identify the title/topic and list the sequence of events in this poem.

SUMMARIZING AS YOU READ

In a Nutshell

(fore • words) Writing and reading are closely connected. We learn about writing by reading, and our appreciation of reading increases through writing. The **summary** is a special form of writing that helps us better appreciate and remember reading material. Read on and learn more about this useful reading and learning strategy.

> Complete the following chart by reading the opening page to "Writing a Summary" in your handbook. (Refer to "Summary, writing the" in the index.)

Guidelines for Writing a Summary

Skim the selection first to get _____ .

Read the selection carefully, paying _____

_____ phrases.

List the main ideas _____

_____ selection!

Review the selection _____ time.

Write a summary of _____

_____ words.

Check your summary for _____ conciseness.

In Sum

> On your own paper, apply the guidelines for summarizing to "Writing Naturally" (two pages) in your handbook. (Share your results.)

Note: By "apply," we mean to follow all of the steps listed above. Begin by skimming the material, follow with a careful reading, then list the main ideas, and so on.

(after • words) Submit a brief but interesting newspaper or magazine article for a class summary-writing activity. (Your class or writing group will decide which article to summarize first.)

READING MAPS

What in the world . . . ?

(fore • words) Some people are atlas addicts. They love pouring over maps of all kinds. Maybe it's the gypsy in them, the desire to travel to far and exotic places. Other people are much more practical about maps and refer to them only when they need to. No matter what your map-reading preferences might be, you'll enjoy the following activity.

❏ If Greece lost its job and had to relocate, would it feel more comfortable (climatewise, that is) near Austria or Spain? If you know your geography or referred to the map section in your handbook, you know the answer is Spain.

▍**Let's see how you can do on four more questions that test your map-reading ability.**

1. If the United Kingdom (minus Northern Ireland) stood on its head, would the city of London be north or south of the Netherlands?

    _____

2. If Italy kicked Sicily across the Mediterranean Sea, which country in Africa would it hit?

    _____

3. If the Czech Republic suddenly decided to live "on the water," what small sea directly south of it might a realtor recommend?

    _____

4. If Belgium became bored with its present location and traded places with an island at 40° N latitude and 8° E longitude, what island would that be?

    _____

(after • words) You and a partner each select a different continent and write four interesting questions about it. (Make sure you refer to the map of this continent in your handbook.) Then exchange your work and try to answer each other's questions.

READING PICTURES

The Editorial Cartoon

(fore • words) Editorial cartoons are found in nearly every large city newspaper. Each cartoon is drawn and "captioned" (words put under the picture) by someone who is trying to make a point or send a message about an important current event.

▌ **Find an editorial cartoon and attach it to this sheet. Then provide the following information about your cartoon:**

Name of the Cartoonist _____

Name of the Newspaper _____

The General Subject of the Cartoon _____

_____

_____

This Cartoonist's Message or Point About the Subject

_____

_____

_____

_____

_____

_____

_____

_____

_____

▌ **Share cartoons among classmates. Notice the wide variety of topics, styles, characters, and captions in the cartoons.**

(after • words) Create your own editorial cartoon about an important issue that directly affects you. This can be something like your student council's decision to have a disc jockey for the next dance . . . or the cliques in your school. Or it can be a community-related issue like the lack of things for young people to do in your city . . . or the state of your city's downtown area. You get the picture, right?

READING GRAPHS

A picture is worth . . .

(fore • words) Graphs are pictures of information. They help us see how two or more things are related. The type of graph that is used depends upon the type of information you are working with.

▌ Read the section on graphs in your handbook. (Refer to "Graphs" in the index.) Then, in the space provided below, list the three basic types of graphs. Also identify one or two important features of each type. (Share your work.)

_____ : _____

_____ : _____

_____ : _____

▌ Study the model graph and then answer the questions listed below and on the next page. (Share your responses.)

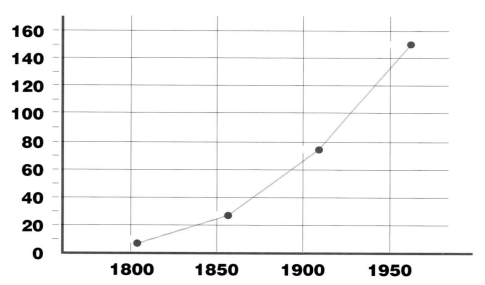

U.S. Population (in millions)

Questions:

1. What is the subject of this line graph? _____

2. How many years are covered in this graph? _____

3. What was the approximate U.S. population in 1850?_____ In 1950? _____

    (To check your answers to number 3, refer to the historical time line in your handbook.)

■ **After you carefully review this model graph, answer the questions that follow. (Share your work.)**

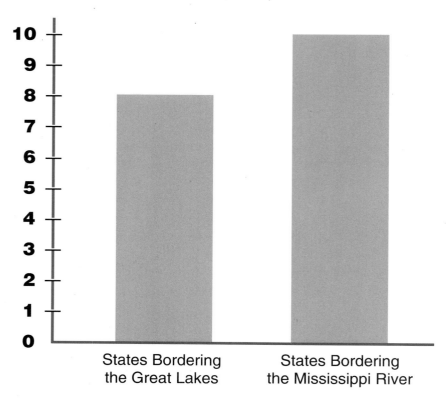

States Bordering
the Great Lakes

States Bordering
the Mississippi River

Questions:

1. What kind of graph is this? _____

2. What two things are being compared?

_____

_____

3. What can you learn from this graph?

_____

_____

Special Challenge: Study a graph in one of your textbooks, in a reference book, or in a newspaper. Learn as much as you can about it. Then share your analysis with a small group of classmates.

(after • words)
Now that you've studied two (or more) graphs, it's your turn to create one. Decide on the subject of your graph by looking in the handbook map section for ideas. (*An example subject:* a comparison between the number of states bordering the Atlantic Ocean and the number of states bordering the Pacific Ocean.)

TALKING AND LISTENING ACTIVITIES

Getting Started

Oral and Aural Learning

(fore•words) You've all heard the old saying, "Talk is cheap." This might be true some of the time, when you speak before you think, but generally talk is anything but cheap. The first set of **Talking and Listening Activities** proves that talk is often worth its weight in gold (as that old saying goes). You'll be asked, among other things, to talk about memorable events, important people, creative situations, and fellow classmates. There's nothing shabby about this type of talk; these are all reasons to celebrate speech. So get ready for some "heady communicatin'."

In the second set of activities, you'll be asked to listen for important facts and details in a news article, in a set of directions, and in a story. We like to think that these activities are worth their weight in gold as well.

It takes practice to become a good listener, and listening is an important learning skill. ("Aural" in the subtitle above refers to the sense of hearing.)

Special Note: Refer to the "Speaking and Listening to Learn" section in your handbook for information on preparing speeches, reading out loud, listening, and interviewing.

User's Checklist

Check your progress as you work on these **Talking and Listening Activities.**

- [ ] **Introducing a Person** • *"And if elected . . . !"*

- [ ] **Public Service Announcement** • *In the Public Interest*

- [ ] **Interviewing a Classmate** • *"Let's talk about it."*

- [ ] **Speaking Persuasively** • *"On behalf of the others . . ."*

- [ ] **Listening for Facts** • *"Just the facts, ma'am."*

- [ ] **Following Directions** • *"I'll only say this once."*

- [ ] **Listening for Details** • *"That doesn't sound right!"*

(after • words) Remember: Your language is a "whole language" made up of five inter-connected parts: *reading, writing, speaking, listening,* and *thinking.* Give a fair amount of attention to all five parts and become a real student of your language.

INTRODUCING A PERSON

Handbook Helper

Read over the information in your handbook on writing and delivering a speech before you begin. (See "Speech skills" in the index.)

"And if elected . . . !"

One of your classmates has decided to run for student council president (or a similar office in your school). Your classmate has asked you to help run the campaign and, in particular, wants you to write his or her nomination speech. This is the speech which introduces the candidate and tells the voters (classmates) why they should vote for him or her.

Write a nomination speech for your classmate. Be sure to mention all of those qualities your candidate has which would make him or her a good student council president.

❑ Is he or she a hard worker? a good student? an honest person? a cooperative person?
❑ What personal examples can you give of just how honest, cooperative, and determined your candidate is?

Read your speech for the class (or for your group). Be sure to put some enthusiasm in your voice!

PUBLIC SERVICE ANNOUNCEMENT

In the Public Interest

Write a short PSA (Public Service Announcement) for a local charity or nonprofit group which could be read on the radio. Your PSA might include a time and place for an event (run, bike-a-thon, read-a-thon, etc.), but it should also contain a message which is strong or "touching" enough to make your listener want to get involved. (It should last between 10 and 15 seconds.)

Helpful HINT

Begin your PSA with a powerful or interesting statement: *"Did you know that last year over one million children . . . ?"* After you clarify or explain your opening statement, tell your listener what he or she can do to help. End with a strong personal appeal.

(after • words) Read your PSA to the class. Try to make it sound like you are actually reading it on the radio. Put lots of color and emotion in your voice. (See "Oral reading" in the handbook index for more reading suggestions.)

INTERVIEWING A CLASSMATE

"Let's talk about it."

TIP: You may look back in the reading at any time during the interview. Also be sure to encourage each other during the interview with hints and prompts.

(fore • words) One of the most efficient ways to learn about something is to talk about it. Another very helpful way to learn is to write down questions. Interviewing a classmate combines these two methods to give you a powerful learning opportunity.

> After reading a selection, your teacher will pair you with a classmate. One of you will be the *interviewer* (the one who asks questions about the reading), and the other one will be the *interviewee* (the one who gives answers).

❏ If you are the interviewer . . .

1. Write as many questions as you can about what you just read.
2. Include some questions that ask for an opinion or a reaction.
3. Choose the question you want to start with.
4. Begin the interview. (You will have 5 to 10 minutes for the interview.) Take notes on the answers you receive.

❏ If you are the interviewee . . .

1. Choose several "writing-to-learn" techniques and do them. This will help you sort, organize, and think about what you read so you will be prepared to answer a variety of questions.
   - ■ You might write freely.
   - ■ You might cluster.
   - ■ You might write an imaginary dialogue.
   - ■ Or you might select one of the writing-to-learn techniques found in the "Classroom Skills" section of your handbook.
2. Use your writings during the interview if you wish. Answer all questions to the best of your ability.

(after • words) Your teacher may ask you either to state the most important points that came out of the interview or to list them on a master sheet which will then be shared and discussed with the class.

SPEAKING PERSUASIVELY

Handbook Helper

Refer to the "Writing to Persuade" section in your handbook for suggestions on organizing and expressing your thoughts.

"On behalf of the others . . ."

You have been selected by your classmates to present a list of concerns to the faculty (principals and teachers) at their next meeting. These concerns are the result of new rules/policies which the faculty may vote into effect at this meeting, rules which you and your classmates feel are very unfair. The faculty has agreed to listen to your arguments against the rule changes so long as you also present some other possible solutions to the problem.

Begin by imagining what this new rule or policy might be (no more field trips, for example) and why the faculty feels it necessary to make this change (no funds available? behavior is a problem?). Then consider other solutions to this problem, ones which both faculty and students could live with. Make your presentation sincere and straightforward.

LISTENING FOR FACTS

Listen up!

An important listening skill is the ability to pull important facts out of what you hear and arrange them in a way which will help you remember them. This work-shop lesson will help you do just that. (Review 402-404 in your hand-book before you try this activity.)

"Just the facts, ma'am."

Your teacher will read you a newspaper article. LISTEN to find *who, when, where,* and *what*. Take brief notes on your own paper while your teacher is reading. Then RECORD your answers on the lines below. (Exchange your work with a classmate and discuss the results.)

1. Who is the article about? _____

2. When did it take place? _____

3. Where? _____

4. What happened? _____

Your teacher will read another newspaper article. FILL IN the blanks as you learn the *who, when, where, what, why,* and *how* of the article. If there is more than one answer, place the most impor-tant answer first in your list. (Share results.) *Note:* It may happen that not all 5 W's and H will be given in the article.

1. Who? _____

2. When? _____

3. Where? _____

4. What? _____

5. Why? _____

    _____

6. How? _____

    _____

FOLLOWING DIRECTIONS

Listen up!

How often have you sat down, ready to begin an assignment, only to be confused because you could not remember exactly what the teacher instructed you to do? How many times have you made mistakes because you did not listen carefully or remember directions? Your ability to follow directions is certainly a basic study skill, one you will want to continue to improve.

"I'll only say this once."

LISTEN carefully to the first set of six directions which your teacher will read to you. Just listen; do not follow the directions yet. When all six directions have been read, the teacher will read each direction again, pause, and give you time to follow the direction by filling in one of the squares below.

Next the teacher will read a second set of six directions to be followed in the squares below. This time the teacher will not "preview" the directions for you. The teacher will read each direction only once, then pause for you to follow the direction.

LISTENING FOR DETAILS

Listen up!

The first step in improving your listening skills is to practice *paying full attention* to what a speaker is saying. If you allow your mind to wander, you will miss part of what is being said. This, in turn, makes it difficult to understand the overall point the speaker is trying to make. The result is frustration for both the speaker and the listener.

"That doesn't sound right!"

LISTEN carefully to the short story which your teacher will read to you. FIND five words that do not make good sense. Try to REMEM-BER the five words in the order in which they are used in the story. WRITE the five words down in order on the numbered blanks below, but only *after* the teacher has finished reading the story. Use the other groups of blanks for the second and final try.

Story 1

1. _____

2. _____

3. _____

4. _____

5. _____

Story 2

1. _____

2. _____

3. _____

4. _____

5. _____

6. _____

Story 3

1. _____

2. _____

3. _____

4. _____

5. _____

6. _____

7. _____

(after • words) See "Listening Skills" in your handbook to further improve your listening skills.

THINKING WORKSHOPS

Figuring Things Out for Yourself

(fore•words) Your handbook lists a number of good reasons to think: (1) thinking saves time, (2) thinking prevents accidents, (3) thinking leads to success, (4) thinking can be fun, and so on. But the most important reason is that *thinking helps you figure things out.* And if you're like everybody else, you have lots to figure out.

The 15 **Thinking Workshops** will give you practice *solving problems, forming understanding, making decisions, evaluating information,* and *building arguments*—and they are guaranteed to do so in enjoyable ways. One activity asks you to figure out what's inside a mysterious small box. Another activity has you enter an interesting contest. Still another one asks you to plan the governor's visit to your school. You'll find a healthy blend of creative, logical, and clear thinking called for in the 15 workshops, so be prepared to "bend your mind" in some interesting ways as you work your way through each one.

Special Note: Refer to "Thinking to Learn" in your handbook for everything you will need to know about the thinking process—and then some. You'll find information about thinking better, thinking and writing, thinking creatively, thinking logically, and using your brain.

User's Checklist

Check your progress as you work on these **Thinking Workshops.**

■ **Solving Problems**

☐ *Making Basic Thinking Moves* • *Plain Brown Wrapper*

☐ *Becoming a Better Thinker* • *Wait for the thought-winds to blow.*

☐ **Clarifying "Fuzzy" Questions** • *"It all depends . . ."*

☐ **Goal Setting, Planning** • *Contest Contest*

■ **Forming Understanding**

☐ **Synthesizing, Focusing, Writing** • *Red Light, Green Light*

☐ **Creative Questions** • *The Visitor from Planet X*

☐ **Observing, Analyzing** • *Elementary, My Dear Watson*

☐ **Making Connections** • *It's a small world.*

☐ **Analyzing Cause and Effect** • *Magma, rising to the crater, all the livelong day . . .*

■ **Making Decisions**

☐ *Inventing* • *Are you game?*

☐ *Creating and Judging* • *Out at the Plate*

☐ **Setting Goals** • *Ready? Aim.*

■ **Evaluating Information**

☐ **Planning and Evaluating** • *The Governor's Visit*

☐ **Choosing and Evaluating** • *Do we measure up?*

■ **Building Arguments**

☐ **Analyzing and Translating** • *Talking Ads*

(after • words) Our hope is that you become more thoughtful after working through these activities and strategies and that you apply what you have learned to figure out problems, make decisions, and build arguments.

MAKING BASIC THINKING MOVES

Plain Brown Wrapper

Suppose one day you come to school and find a small box in a plain brown wrapper sitting on your desk. You have no idea who put it there or why. Is it a bomb? Is it a gift from a secret admirer? Did someone lose it? What's inside?

If you turn to section 310 in *Write Source 2000*, you will find a chart that shows many ways to think through a problem. Notice all the basic types of thinking people can do. Under each basic type, notice the list of different methods or approaches.

Use the chart in section 310 to help you solve the puzzle of the box in the plain brown wrapper. Below, you will see a list of the nine main "thinking moves" which are named in the chart. For each heading, write down the approach that you think would be most helpful in solving the puzzle. Then say why you chose it. The first one is done for you. (Of course, you won't be able to come up with a real answer because this is an imaginary problem. The important thing is to understand how to go about thinking.)

OBSERVE: _____*Listen*_____ | *If I shake the box, I might hear something inside that sounds familiar.*

GATHER: _____*Interview others*_____ |

QUESTION: _____ |

FOCUS: _____ |

ORGANIZE: _____

_____

_____

ANALYZE: _____

_____

_____

IMAGINE: _____

_____

_____

RETHINK: _____

_____

_____

EVALUATE: _____

_____

_____

When you've finished making your list above, go back over it. Find one answer that could be improved. Write your improvement below:

_____

_____

_____

(after • thought) Use the same "thinking moves" the next time you are asked to think, write, or solve a problem.

BECOMING A BETTER THINKER

Wait for the thought-winds to blow.

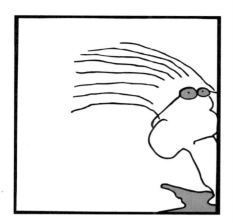

Is there any problem in your life right now that is forcing you to think?

Write Source 2000 has some help for you. Turn to the "Thinking Better" section and read how a "bad thinker" would flub up if he or she were you. Now turn to the next page and read the 10 things that a good thinker would do.

Here's a way to remember how to become a better thinker. Turn the 10 instructions into a poem. Address the poem to yourself. For the first line, say something to yourself that means "Be patient." But use more poetic language. (For example, you might say, "Wait for the thought-winds to blow.") For the second line, use poetic words to tell yourself to "Set goals." Go through all 10 points in the same way. (If you want to, write a finishing line for your poem.)

(Title) _____

1. _____

2. _____

3. _____

4. _____

5. _____

6. _____

7. _____

8. _____

9. _____

10. _____

(after • thought) If you are inspired to learn more about poetry, read the sections about poetry in *Write Source 2000*.

CLARIFYING "FUZZY" QUESTIONS

"It all depends . . ."

Here is a big "fuzzy" question for you to think about:

Should you try to help if you see someone seriously hurt in an accident?

This question affects many people's lives, and nobody fully knows the answer to it.

"If I came upon a serious accident? Well, it all depends . . ."

All of the following thinking methods can be useful for clarifying "fuzzy" questions. Use any THREE to get yourself ready to write. (Do this on another sheet of paper.)

- ❑ **Get the whole picture**—in other words, remind yourself of everyone who is somehow involved.
- ❑ **Argue**, in turn, for **both sides** of the question (yes and no).
- ❑ **Create a model** (an imagined or hypothetical accident) to simplify the problem.
- ❑ **Pose the problem** to yourself **in a new way**. ("If *I* were in an accident . . .")
- ❑ **Rephrase the question**.
- ❑ **Question your assumptions** (the thoughts you take for granted).
- ❑ **Create an analogy** or a useful new metaphor. (Compare an accident victim to a . . .)
- ❑ **Create a "worst-case" and a "best-case" scenario**. (Take the possibilities to the edge: What's the worst that could happen? What's the best?)

After you have chosen three of these methods and made notes on your thinking, WRITE your best ideas on the subject.

THINKING IT THROUGH

(after • thought) Think up a "fuzzy" question (or two or three) you would like someone else to answer.

GOAL SETTING, PLANNING

Contest Contest

Suppose you have entered a contest: "**$150 prize to the student who designs the best contest which draws attention to a community-wide issue. Your contest plan must include the following:**
1) *aims:* **what you hope to accomplish,**
2) *rules:* **who can enter and how often,**
3) *procedures:* **how you go about entering the contest,**
4) *judges:* **who will judge the contest,**
5) *criteria for judging:* **how the judges will decide which contest is the best, and**
6) *awards:* **what awards or prizes will be given.**"

What community-wide issues are you aware of? Litter? Crowded schools? Vandalism? Gangs? Drunken driving? Child neglect? Animal abuse? Homelessness? Bicycle theft? Air pollution?

Plan the contest that you (or your small group) would turn in to win the $150. Choose one serious problem. Then, try to come up with an interesting form of competition that draws attention to the problem and might even lead to a solution. To make a strong impression, offer a unique grand prize, a prize that calls attention to the problem in a humorous or interesting way. (Besides writing down your plan, give your contest a catchy title.)

THINKING IT THROUGH

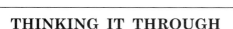

✔ Think about the many different types of contests you might be able to change slightly and use for your own contest: essay contests, poster contests, speech contests, bicycle or running races, door-to-door sales, art contests, bake-offs, poetry contests, eating contests, sports contests, wacky world's record contests, etc.

(after • thought) With your teacher's permission, have a real "contest contest" in your classroom. Decide together whether teachers or students should pick the winner. When you have selected a winning plan for a contest, how about actually *holding* that contest for students at your school?

SYNTHESIZING, FOCUSING, WRITING

Red Light, Green Light

Here's a stop-and-go exercise that will help you to shape information into new forms (that's called "synthesizing").

GO back into your memory and recall exactly what it felt like to sit in your class on the first day of this school year.

STOP and write down your memories of that time, focusing on sights, sounds, feelings, smells, tastes, and whatever else you remember.

_____

_____

_____

_____

_____

_____

_____

_____

_____

_____

_____

_____

_____

GO to _Write Source 2000_, sections 324-326, and read what it means to "synthesize information."

STOP and write down what you think it means to "synthesize information."

_____

_____

_____

GO to the "Observation Report" section in your handbook and read the "Model Observation Report," a description of a passenger's experience as his plane is readied for takeoff. Pay attention to the details and to the way they are organized.

STOP and write, once again, about your first day of class. But this time, use the airplane report to give you new ideas for shaping your description. (Psst! Don't look now, but you're synthesizing!)

_____

_____

_____

_____

_____

_____

_____

_____

_____

_____

_____

_____

(after • thought) Use the same stop-and-go strategy the next time you are asked to "synthesize."

CREATIVE QUESTIONS

The Visitor from Planet X

▌A spacecraft lands in your backyard, and when you
investigate, you come face to face with a being from
another planet. Write seven questions you would ask
this visitor.

Q1 _____

_____

Q2 _____

_____

Q3 _____

_____

Q4 _____

_____

Q5 _____

_____

Q6 _____

_____

Q7 _____

_____

(after • thought) Have the visitor provide answers. (How about switching papers
with a partner? Imagine that you're the visitor and answer your partner's questions.)
Or . . . have the visitor write a letter to friends back on his/her home planet telling
about Earth and how it differs from the visitor's home planet.

OBSERVING, ANALYZING

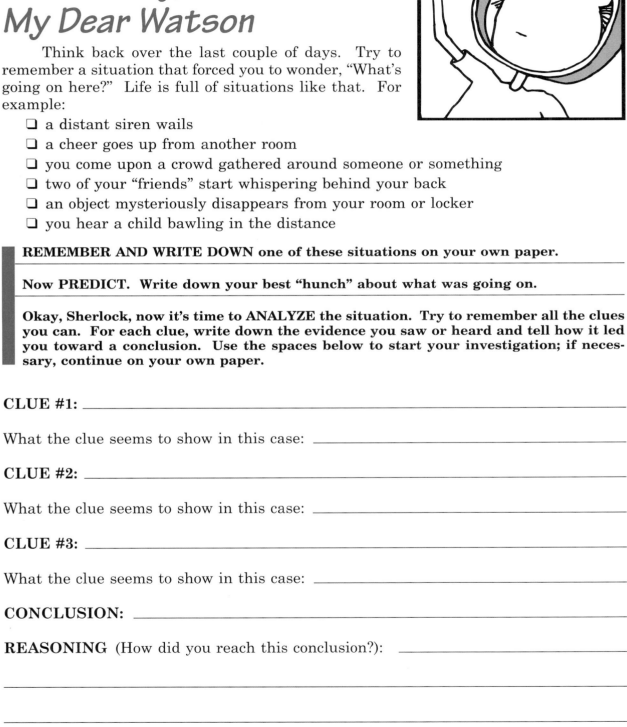

Elementary, My Dear Watson

Think back over the last couple of days. Try to remember a situation that forced you to wonder, "What's going on here?" Life is full of situations like that. For example:

- ❏ a distant siren wails
- ❏ a cheer goes up from another room
- ❏ you come upon a crowd gathered around someone or something
- ❏ two of your "friends" start whispering behind your back
- ❏ an object mysteriously disappears from your room or locker
- ❏ you hear a child bawling in the distance

REMEMBER AND WRITE DOWN one of these situations on your own paper.

Now PREDICT. Write down your best "hunch" about what was going on.

Okay, Sherlock, now it's time to ANALYZE the situation. Try to remember all the clues you can. For each clue, write down the evidence you saw or heard and tell how it led you toward a conclusion. Use the spaces below to start your investigation; if necessary, continue on your own paper.

CLUE #1: _____

What the clue seems to show in this case: _____

CLUE #2: _____

What the clue seems to show in this case: _____

CLUE #3: _____

What the clue seems to show in this case: _____

CONCLUSION: _____

REASONING (How did you reach this conclusion?): _____

_____

_____

MAKING CONNECTIONS

It's a small world.

█ Begin by listing eight current national or world problems. (Use a newspaper or magazine if necessary.)

1. _____

2. _____

3. _____   6. _____

4. _____   7. _____

5. _____   8. _____

█ Select one of the topics which seems to have little or nothing to do with you and your immediate world. Then find a way to connect it. Maybe you could see no reason to worry about a drought in California or Texas until you realized you will now be paying much more for your favorite fruit drink. Or maybe you can't at first understand why there's so much fuss in this country over problems in Central America or the Middle East.

Problem: _____

Connection: _____

_____

_____

THINKING IT THROUGH

Here are some of the possible connections you may discover: A causes B, A is similar to B, A results from B, A and B are both like C, A is a sign of B, A is a by-product of B, A is part of B, etc.

(after • thought) Connect as many of the other seven topics as you can. Find some new topics if you run out of ideas.

ANALYZING CAUSE AND EFFECT

Magma, rising to the crater, all the livelong day . . .

Your textbooks in school are full of explanations of the causes and effects of things. Volcanoes, lightning, the Civil War, acid rain, drug abuse, sand dunes, the atom bomb, and on and on.

Find an explanation of something interesting in one of your textbooks. *(For example, why do volcanoes blow their tops? Why do whales sing?)* **If you can't find an interesting explanation in your textbooks, turn to an encyclopedia in your classroom or library. Read carefully, step by step, until you understand the whole cause-effect sequence. Pay special attention to any diagrams you find.**

Now for the hard part—and the fun part! Explain the cause and effect process you learned about, but do it in the form of a rap or a poem. (If you choose a poem, consider writing it so that it can be sung to the tune of either "I've Been Working on the Railroad" or "America the Beautiful.")

THINKING IT THROUGH

■ Setting words to a rap beat or familiar tune will force you to sort through all the words you know that relate to the subject. You'll have to think about their meaning as well as their rhythm and sound. It would be helpful to make a list of all the special terms that relate to your topic.

■ You will need to do some creative thinking for this exercise. It will be easier if you work with a partner and bounce your ideas back and forth.

(after • thought) Practice your rap or song a few times; work out the bugs; and, when you're ready, sing it. Better yet, hand out the words and have your whole class sing it. You'll be surprised how long you will remember your song.

INVENTING

Are you game?

For 20 years Mr. Sporto and his gym classes have batted, tumbled, and kicked with gusto. But 20 years is a long time, and Mr. Sporto is losing some of his enthusiasm. What he needs is a new game, a game that will renew the competitive fire in his eyes.

CREATE a new game or sport for Mr. Sporto, and if it actually provides both recreation and exercise, he just might use it next semester. (Work in groups if your teacher allows it.) Use the space provided for initial planning. The final draft explaining your new game should be neatly written on your own paper. (What should you consider in your planning? How about the object of this game, the name, the equipment needed, the rules, and so on?)

A BETTER GAME

_____

_____

_____

_____

_____

_____

_____

_____

_____

_____

_____

(after • thought) Play the game! Perhaps you could even demonstrate the game for the class or for your gym teacher.

CREATING AND JUDGING

Out at the Plate

A major U.S. publisher has asked you to write your autobiography. (For tips on writing autobiographies, see *Write Source 2000.*) You've written your book, and it looks like a possible best-seller. Only one problem: you haven't thought of a title yet.

To start with, think of five possible titles. If your life has been a series of adventures followed by disappointments, you might call your book *Out at the Plate.* Write your own five best ideas here:

#1 _____

#2 _____

#3 _____

#4 _____

#5 _____

In order to choose the best one, you'll have to sort, sift, and select. In other words, you'll have to rank the titles, judge them, and choose the best. For general guidance on "Studying and Evaluating a Subject," turn to *Write Source 2000*, sections 327-329. To reach a decision, use the letters of the words "I   D•E•C•I•D•E." Here's how:

DECISION-MAKING STRATEGY: **I DECIDE**

I means **Imagine** the outcome. In other words, consider what a great title *is*. Write your ideas on the lines below. (TIP: See *Write Source 2000*, 025, for guidelines on writing titles.)

A great title is short, _____

_____

D means **Define** your goal. In this case, that's easy: *to choose the best title for my autobiography.*

E means **Enumerate** or list your options. (You did that above when you wrote down your five best possible titles.)

C means **Choose** two or three best options. Write your top choices here:

#1 _____

#2 _____

#3 _____

I means **Investigate** the options. In other words, try out each title. How do you like it? What does it mean? How do others like it? Which title best matches the criteria you wrote when you "imagined the outcome"? Write what you like and dislike about each of the options on the lines below:

#1 _____

_____

#2 _____

_____

#3 _____

_____

D means **Decide** on the best option. Which one comes closest to your original idea of a good title? Write your choice below:

_____

E means **Evaluate** your choice. Explain below why you chose it:

_____

_____

_____

(after • thought) Reflect on your choice. How do you feel about it? How do others react? Review all the steps you took, and if you aren't satisfied, run through it again.

SETTING GOALS

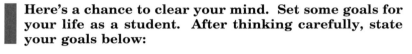

Do the school days ever seem to slide by like foam on a lazy stream? Do you ever ask, "What am I doing here in this school? And where am I going?"

Here's a chance to clear your mind. Set some goals for your life as a student. After thinking carefully, state your goals below:

◾ First, name three of your best personality traits, qualities, or skills that you think will help you later in your life:

(1) _____ (2) _____ (3) _____

◾ State a major goal for your **life**—what do you hope to be remembered for?

_____

◾ State a goal for your whole **career** as a student, a goal which will help you to achieve the major life-goal you stated above:

_____

◾ State a goal for **this year** which will help you achieve the goal you stated above for your whole career as a student:

_____

◾ State a goal for **this week** that will help you achieve your goal for this year in school:

_____

◾ State a goal for **today** that will help you achieve the goal you stated for this week:

_____

THINKING IT THROUGH

You will find plenty of good advice for setting goals in the "Individual Skills" section of *Write Source 2000*. While you're at it, sneak a peek at the other information on managing time, completing assignments, and managing stress.

(after • thought) What, in your opinion, would be good reasons for you to abandon your original set of goals and set up new ones in their place?

PLANNING AND EVALUATING

The Governor's Visit

The governor of your state has decided to visit five schools to get a firsthand look at education today. Your school has been selected. His advance team has told you he will spend two hours at your school (from 10:00 until noon).

Your class is one of the classes selected to plan the governor's visit from beginning to end. The principal will select the best plan. It seems every student and teacher wants an opportunity to meet the governor. The mayor and Senator Hillis (who lives in your community) have sent word that they are expecting to be present.

Plan the governor's visit and fill in your final schedule below. Remember, he wants to find out as much as he can about what works and what needs to be changed in today's schools. Consider the best possible ways to let the governor see (or understand in some way) what does or does not work well in your school.

THE GOVERNOR'S VISIT

10:00 _____   11:00 _____

_____   _____

10:15 _____   11:15 _____

_____   _____

10:30 _____   11:30 _____

_____   _____

10:45 _____   11:45 _____

_____   _____

(after • thought) Get together with a partner and compile a list of suggestions for improving education in our country today. (This may include any or all levels of school—from preschool through college.)

CHOOSING AND EVALUATING

Do we measure up?

This activity will help you become more sensitive to the thoughts and experiences of other individuals. More specifically, this activity will help you better appreciate school life as someone else might.

Here's what you should do: Look through the eyes of a person in your school who must use a wheelchair.

- What do you see?
- From the morning, when you roll through the front door of your school, to the afternoon, when you roll back out, what do you experience?
- Are the drinking fountains low enough? Can you turn around in the bathroom? Can you get from floor to floor? Can you reach books in the library?

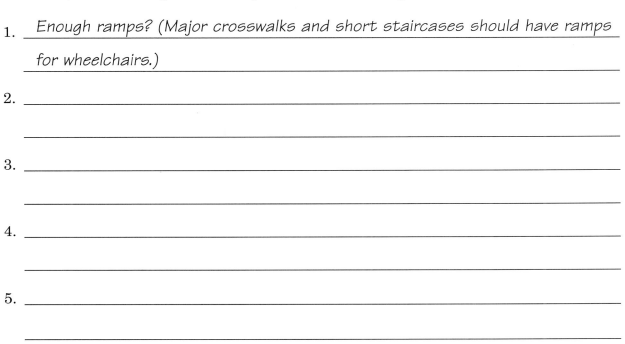

Getting a drink is a tall order for some people.

Now that you've thought about it, how well is your school equipped for a person in a wheelchair? **EVALUATE** your school. First choose five points that you think should be measured or tested (the first one is supplied to give you the idea). After each measure you come up with, explain what it would mean for the school to be well equipped in that area. (See the example below in parentheses.) Share your results with classmates.

1. _Enough ramps? (Major crosswalks and short staircases should have ramps_
   for wheelchairs.)

2. _____

   _____

3. _____

   _____

4. _____

   _____

5. _____

   _____

(after • thought) Evaluate your school's "accessibility" to individuals in wheelchairs using each one of the five criteria. Write your results in essay form on your own paper. (See "Developing the School Essay" and "Judging Information" for guidelines.)

ANALYZING AND TRANSLATING

Talking Ads

What if an advertisement could talk? What would it **really** say?

Find a popular magazine like *Time, Newsweek, U.S. News, People,* or *Seventeen*. In it, choose an interesting advertisement for a car, perfume, jeans, or shoes. Study your ad very carefully until you think you know everything that it is "secretly" saying to you to get you to buy the product. Now switch roles. Pretend *you* are the ad, and you're doing the talking. Write your secret message below, starting with the following words:

"If you buy (name of product), . . ."

THINKING IT THROUGH

✔ Have you studied your ad carefully enough? Have you noticed the big type, the small type, the people in the pictures, the objects they hold, the background?

✔ Many advertisements are based on a "little white lie"—a false promise that if you use the product, you will miraculously be changed into something different or better than you are. Can you detect a "little white lie" in your ad?

✔ Have you caught any **humor** or **puns** in the ad?

(after • thought) Make up an ad of your own for the same product, but change the target audience. For example, if young men were the audience for the first ad, aim yours at middle-aged mothers or senior citizens. Be as persuasive as you can. Use scissors, paste, and drawing tools.

VOCABULARY AND WORD PLAY ACTIVITIES

Getting Started

Language Building

(fore • words) You've probably heard the saying, "All work and no play makes Johnny a dull boy." Well, we don't want you to work too hard, and we certainly don't want any dull boys or girls. We want you to have fun with your language, to take risks with it, to bend and stretch it in new ways. And that's just what you'll do in the **Word Play Activities**. You'll see, among other things, how many action words you can link, how many sound words you can list, and how many riddles you can write.

Because we ask you to "play" with words doesn't mean that the language is not important to us. We know that exploring and experimenting with words makes you a better language user. Translation: Working through the word play activities will help you write and speak more effectively.

In the **Vocabulary Activities**, you will increase your knowledge of words and word parts. You'll *learn about* and *work with* the most important prefixes and roots in our language. So, whenever you come across words you're unsure of, you'll have a strategy for figuring out what they mean.

Special Note: the "Improving Vocabulary" chapter in your handbook contains detailed lists of prefixes, suffixes, and roots. Make good use of these lists when you work on the activities that follow and whenever you stumble upon new and challenging words in your reading.

User's Checklist

Check your progress as you work on these **Vocabulary and Word Play Activities.**

☐ **Linking Verbs** • *Chain Letters*

☐ **On-o-mat-o-poe-ia** • *SPLAT is when a hippo does a belly flop.*

☐ **Doublets** • *From "bald" to "hair" in five easy steps!*

☐ **Writing Riddles** • *Fuddle, Muddle, & Bamboozle*

☐ **Word Bank** • *Dry words, wet words . . .*

☐ **Using Word Parts** • *Bicycles, binoculars, biscuits . . .*

☐ **Using Prefixes** • *14 Prefixes . . . 4,000 Words!*

☐ **Using Roots** • *Divide and Conquer*

☐ **Using Prefixes and Roots** • *Building Words*

(after • words) Become a student of your language. What do we mean by that? Keep your eyes and ears open for new and interesting words, well-put ideas, and eye-opening conversations and scenes. Make note of these "language bytes" in a small notepad so you won't forget them. Later, when a piece of tired writing needs a face-lift, you can refer to your list of language bytes for some "face-saving" words and ideas.

LINKING VERBS

Chain Letters

Let's see how many "vivid" action verbs you can connect. *(The last letter of one verb becomes the first letter of the next one.)* A verb chain has been started for you. Share your work after you fill in your last link. See who came up with the most interesting list of words.

Remember: Your verbs must be vivid—*gobble*, not *eat*; *stare*, not *look*.

SPECIAL CHALLENGE

See if you can complete your chain with a vivid verb that ends with the letter "l"; that way, the verbs are truly "linked" together.

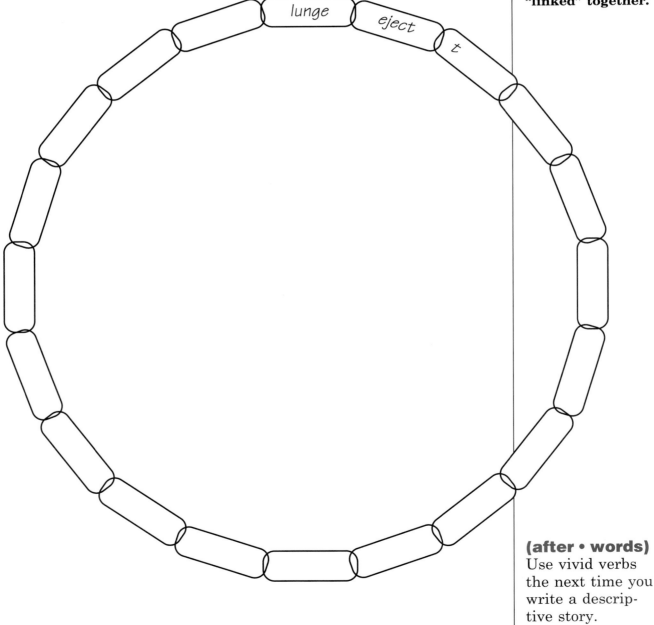

(after • words)
Use vivid verbs the next time you write a descriptive story.

ON-O-MAT-O-POE-IA

SPLAT is when a hippo does a belly flop.

We have many words in our language which stand for sounds. (The formal literary term for such words is *onomatopoeia.*) For example, you know that *buzz* stands for the sound made by a bee, and *sizzle* stands for the sound made by frying food. Other common sound words are *chirp, zing, zip, beep,* and *honk.*

Sound Off

Some sound words in the list below might not be as familiar to you.

■ **Read these words out loud (if your teacher allows it). Put some genuine feeling into your reading so that you can enjoy the true sound of each word.**

■ **Then, add five or more sound words of your own—not obvious ones like *buzz* and *sizzle*, but new and improved ones like *shlumph* and *do-wap*—on the lines below.**

splat	zwat	gunk	whump
gush	shoop	galumph	conk
oomph	pshaw	ding	rat-a-tat
sploosh	poing	slurp	

(after • words)
List ways your favorite sound can be made. Don't limit yourself to obvious ways. A SPLAT can be made when an egg hits the floor; it can also be made when a hippo does a belly flop. Have a contest. See who can come up with the longest list.

DOUBLETS

From "bald" to "hair" in five easy steps!

One of the oldest word games around is the **doublet**. It was introduced by Lewis Carroll (who also wrote *Alice in Wonderland*) more than 100 years ago.

> ▌ **The object is to write a new word that is an opposite (or related in some other way) to the original word by changing only one letter at a time:**

bald

> ball
> hall
> hail

hair

> ▌ **See how well you do with the following doublets.** *Remember:* **You can change only one letter at a time.**

love

cold

page

hate

heat

book

(after • words) Now make up your own doublet. After you've tested it to make sure it works, give the first and last words to a classmate to figure out.

WRITING RIDDLES

Fuddle, Muddle, & Bamboozle

Fuddle, muddle, and **bamboozle** might sound like the stage names for a silly comedy act. These are, in fact, real words which serve well to describe riddles since they mean "to trick." In order to write riddles, you will need some ideas or *data* that you can use to create your "trick questions." To build your data base, create several lists of related words.

Start by listing four general names of things on the bold lines. Choose from occupations, furniture, foods, sports, school, pets, clothes, holidays, and so on. Then list words which come to mind when you think about each of these ideas. (To the left is a list of words which might come to mind when you think of basketball.)

basketball

free throw

field goal

bucket

rim

backboard

foul

dribble

traveling

Riddle Away

Write two (or more) comparison riddles on your own paper. Don't compare two ideas that are too closely alike (as in basketball players and football players); they usually aren't very tricky. Try something like this: "What do basketball players and babies have in common?—They both dribble a lot." Also, write one or two riddles about single ideas: "Why do basketball players stay home all of the time?—It's a penalty to travel."

WORD BANK

Dry words, wet words...

When you're looking for just the right word as you write, you generally refer to a thesaurus or dictionary for help, right? Here's another way you and your classmates can look for special words. You can create a reference word bank. You and a partner should first select one of the special categories listed below (or one of your own choosing) that you would like to work with.

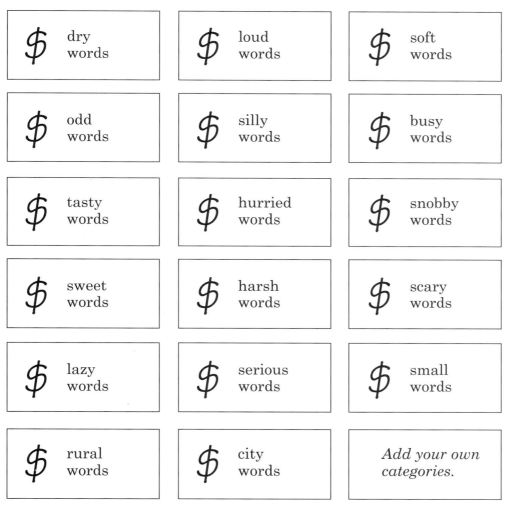

$ dry words	$ loud words	$ soft words
$ odd words	$ silly words	$ busy words
$ tasty words	$ hurried words	$ snobby words
$ sweet words	$ harsh words	$ scary words
$ lazy words	$ serious words	$ small words
$ rural words	$ city words	*Add your own categories.*

Wordstorming

Then brainstorm for words as you think of this category. (For example, three dry words are *parched, gritty,* and *thirsty*.) Push yourselves so your lists contain a variety of interesting words. Ask friends and family members for their ideas.

SPECIAL CHALLENGE

See if you can add to your list at least one word for each letter in the alphabet.

(after • words)
Compile lists for a class word-bank booklet. Refer to the booklet whenever you need words for a special purpose—say, for example, when you're writing a tasty poem or thinking of ways to develop a snobby character in a story.

Tip: Add new words and categories to the word bank throughout the school year.

USING WORD PARTS

Bicycles, binoculars, biscuits . . .

As you already know, many words in our language are made up of word parts (prefixes, suffixes, roots). Knowing some of these word parts can help you figure out the meaning of words you come across in your reading.

How many of the following word parts do you know? Fill in the spaces below with as many words and definitions as you can. Refer to your handbook when you come across a word part you are unsure of.

Word Part	Sample Words	Definitions
tri-		
inter-		
multi-		
hydr-		
leg-		

(after • words)
Continue to look for word parts whenever you come across a word you're not sure of. (This is especially useful in science books.)

USING PREFIXES

14 Prefixes . . . 4,000 Words!

Of the 20,000 most used words in our language, approximately 5,000 begin with prefixes. Over 4,000 of these words use one of only 14 different prefixes. Learn these 14 prefixes, and you are on your way to knowing the definitions of over 4,000 words!

REFER to the "Prefixes" section of your handbook and WRITE the meanings of the following prefixes. Then, think of a sample word which begins with that prefix. (IMPORTANT! Try not to use any word given as a sample in your handbook. A dictionary will help if you're stuck for ideas.)

Prefix	Meaning	Sample Word
ab	*from, away*	*absent*
ad		
bi		
co, con, com		
de		
dis, dif		
em, en		
ex		
in, il, im		
pre		
pro		
re		
sub		
un		

Using what you have just learned, MATCH the following words with the proper definition of each. (You may want to underline each prefix to help make the matching easier.)

Group 1

_____ 1. to stick to   a. immigrant

_____ 2. not steady   b. bilateral

_____ 3. a coming together of people   c. disperse

_____ 4. one in favor of an issue   d. convention

_____ 5. agreement by both sides   e. unstable

_____ 6. one who moves into a country   f. adhere

_____ 7. to break apart   g. proponent

Group 2

_____ 8. under the earth   a. abduct

_____ 9. bring back to life   b. expire

_____ 10. thinking done before an event   c. enduring

_____ 11. take away from   d. subterranean

_____ 12. move down   e. demote

_____ 13. run out of breath   f. resuscitate

_____ 14. lasting in time   g. premeditation

(after • words) Find at least one "new" word for each of these 14 prefixes and bring them to share with the class. You may find them anywhere—in your other schoolwork, the newspaper, a magazine, etc.

USING ROOTS

Divide and Conquer

As you mature, your vocabulary matures and grows, too. Many of the new words you learn from textbooks have their origin, or beginning, in Latin and Greek roots. The study of even a small number of these roots and their meanings can be a great help in building your vocabulary.

▌ **DEFINE the *roots* on the lines below; refer to the "Roots" section of your handbook for those you don't already know.**

aster, astr _____*star*_____   luc, lum _____

chron _____   cred _____

mit, miss _____   dem _____

phon _____   fin _____

port _____   flex, flect _____

stru, struct _____   graph, gram _____

▌ **Using the root meanings you just listed above, FILL IN THE BLANKS below so that each word has a complete definition.**

1. **demo•graph•y** . . . information in ____*written*____ form which

   deals with ____*people*____

2. **syn•chron•ize** . . . arranging two or more items so that they are

   together in _____

3. **dis•credit** . . . something done to take away our _____
   in a person or thing

4. **trans•luc•ent** . . . material which lets _____ pass
   through

5. **trans•mit** . . . to _____ something from one place to another

6. **ob•struct** . . . something which works against _____

7. **in•fin•ite** . . . something which never _____

USING PREFIXES AND ROOTS

Building Words

■ **CREATE AND DEFINE** as many words as you can by combining a prefix and a root from the lists below. You may add endings and other letters as needed.

Prefixes: co (con, com), de, dis, ex, in (il, im, ir)

Roots: cred, duc, fin, mit (miss), port, stru (struct)

WORD	DEFINITION
1. *incredible*	*not able to believe*
2.	
3.	
4.	
5.	
6.	
7.	
8.	
9.	
10.	

(after • words) Set aside a section of your notebook or learning log for prefix-suffix-root word study. Keep track of new or interesting words that contain a word part helpful in remembering the meaning.

PART IV
Writing and Learning Minilessons

Covering the important areas

of writing, language, and learning

included in *Write Source 2000*

MINILESSONS

Bite-Sized Bits of Learning

(fore•words) You all know about Teddy Grahams. Kids across the country can't stop eating these bite-sized treats. Why have they become so popular? A graham cracker is a graham cracker, right? Is it because they are shaped like cute little teddy bears or that they come in a variety of flavors? No, their popularity is in their size. They are just the right size to pop into your mouth, one after another.

We like to think that our **Minilessons** offer learning opportunities that are just the right size. They don't stuff you with seven courses of rules to remember and worksheets to complete, yet they don't necessarily leave you hungry for more information either. It's learning in miniature, one important concept at a time, in 10- or 15-minute segments.

Special Note: We offer a minilesson for nearly every important idea in your handbook. Read through your "User's Checklist" and see for yourself. Also, read through some of the minilessons themselves. You've never seen learning like this before.

User's Checklist

Check your progress as you work on these **Minilessons**.

- ❏ **Journal Writing** • *Club Ed*
- ❏ **Group Advising** • *Kid Gloves*
- ❏ **"Found" Writing Ideas** • *Ten Steps*
- ❏ **Taking Inventory of Your Thoughts** • *All systems are go.*
- ❏ **Offbeat Questions** • *Off the Beaten Path*
- ❏ **Offbeat Questions** • *Offbeat Class*
- ❏ **Writing About Experiences** • *Through Different Lenses*
- ❏ **The Personal Essay** • *What's in a name?*
- ❏ **Personalizing the School Essay** • *Rewards and Punishments*
- ❏ **Agreement with Collective Nouns** • *A Leap of Dolphins*
- ❏ **Improving Your Writing** • *Less is more.*
- ❏ **Improving Your Writing** • *Diet Plan*

Getting Started

❑ **Personal Research** • *Journey to the Center of the Problem*

❑ **Parts of a Book** • *Between Covers*

❑ **Using the Thesaurus** • *Tale, Legend, or Lie?*

❑ **Creative Process** • *My Last Bright Idea*

❑ **Avoid Fuzzy Thinking** • *Fuzzball*

❑ **Context Clues** • *Look around.*

❑ **Kinds of Literature** • *Subjects and Kinds*

❑ **Plot** • *The plot thickens.*

❑ **Interviewing/Creative Collaboration** • *Mind if I tape this?*

❑ **Taking Objective Tests** • *Let's be objective about this.*

❑ **Goal Setting** • *Goal to Go*

❑ **Ellipses** • *911*

❑ **Ellipses** • *Broken Reply*

❑ **Commas Separating Adjectives** • *Stand-Up Commas*

❑ **Semicolons and Colons** • *And Now, for a Short Pause*

❑ **Semicolons** • *Traveling Lightly*

❑ **Semicolons** • *Keeku! Keeku!*

❑ **Dash** • *Superduperphone*

❑ **Hyphens** • *Word Factory*

❑ **Exclamation Points** • *You don't have to shout!*

❑ **Quotation Marks** • *Pssst!*

❑ **Quotation Marks** • *So to Speak*

❑ **Possessives** • *The Hess Family*

❑ **Parentheses** • *Divided Attention*

❑ **Forming Plural Nouns** • *Double Vision*

❑ **Spelling** • *Ice cube rides again.*

❑ **Spotting Subjects and Predicates** • *Door Jam*

❑ **Complete Subjects** • *The Big S*

❑ **Complete Predicates** • *The Big P*

❑ **Identifying Modifiers** • *Did you hear that?*

❑ **Kinds of Sentences** • *The Four Stooges on Venus*

❑ **Types of Nouns** • *Lost and Found (I)*

❑ **Pronouns and Antecedents** • *Lost and Found (II)*

❑ **Kinds of Pronouns** • *And on Your Left*

❑ **Degrees of Adjectives and Adverbs** • *Beyond Awesome, Different, and Cool*

❑ **Forms of Adjectives** • *Three Bears*

❑ **Prepositions** • *Heads and Tails*

❑ **Duolog and Interjections** • *Wow! What? Phew! Oh?*

❑ **Using Time Lines** • *It Changed the World.*

❑ **Using Graphs** • *Graphic Designer*

❑ **Using Tables and Time Lines** • *Presidential Happenings*

❑ **Using Tables** • *Up from Number 2*

❑ **Using Time Lines** • *Two is company.*

❑ **Using Roots** • *Taking Root*

❑ **Writing to Learn** • *Life Lines*

❑ **Setting Goals** • *Follow Through*

❑ **Managing Stress** • *A Stress Test*

(after • words) Write minilessons of your own about writing or language learning to share with members of your writing group or your entire class.

MINILESSONS

Club Ed .... *Journal Writing*   A

■ Wonder how to get started writing in a journal? Why not look over the advice on starting a journal in section **131-132**? Check out the idea of writing in a learning log (more on that in **409**). Then,

> READ the opening pages of *Write Source 2000*, "An Invitation to Learning" (**001-002**). Focus on what the writer means by "Club Ed."

> WRITE in your journal whatever thoughts come to your mind about the "learning" you experience outside the classroom. Don't settle for the first thoughts that pop up. Keep digging. How many kinds of things do you learn "on the outside"? How is learning outside of school different from learning in school? What would learning be like inside school, if you had *your* way?

Kid Gloves .... *Group Advising*   B

■ Want to know how to comment on someone's paper without hurting the author's feelings? Read *Write Source 2000*, sections **028** and **029**, especially the part on "Maintaining Good Relations." Now,

> SUPPOSE you've read a paper with a boring first sentence. Do you say:
> A. Wow, this one's dead on arrival.
> B. Cut out this rotten first sentence. OR
> C. You sure don't write very good beginnings.

> The answer is: "None of the above." All three answers would hurt feelings. Instead, you might say, "I like the essay even better with the first sentence removed."

> Now you're on your own. What do you say if the second paragraph is illogical:
> A. You sure screwed up in the second paragraph.
> B. In the second paragraph, how about building the whole paragraph around the idea in your last sentence?
> C. Man, I don't have a clue what the second paragraph means.

> STATE your best answer and explain why.

> THINK of a tactful thing to say if you discover half a dozen *cliches* in your partner's paper.

Ten Steps .... *"Found" Writing Ideas*   C

■ Look over section **033**, and pay special attention to the subsection " 'Found' Writing Ideas."

> JUMP in the air and SPIN (in the classroom or wherever else your teacher suggests). Don't move your feet when you land.

> TAKE 10 steps in the direction your feet are pointing—of course, you should stop if you come to a wall or any other immovable object.

> WRITE fast and furiously about whatever you see from the point where you stopped.

All systems are go. ...... *Taking Inventory of Your Thoughts*   A

■ Choose a starting point for a new piece of writing using the ideas in section **034**. Try to decide on a topic in 2-3 minutes.

   USE topic number **016**, "Taking Inventory of Your Thoughts," to collect and focus your ideas.

   Quickly JOT down everything you can think of about
   1) your present **situation** as a writer, (What brings you to write about this?)
   2) your **self**, (What would this writing mean for you?)
   3) your **subject**, (What do you know about it?)
   4) your **readers**, (Who are you aiming at?)
   5) your **style** of writing. (What kind of style will best get your subject across to your readers?)

Off the Beaten Path .... *Offbeat Questions*   B

■ Get a feel for the "Offbeat" or "Unstructured" questions in **038**.
   Then WRITE an "offbeat" question (and an offbeat answer) about a certain place, object, or event.
   WRITE two more offbeat questions and answers about your subject; SHARE your work with a classmate.

Offbeat Class .... *Offbeat Questions*   C

■ Get a feeling for the "Offbeat" or "Unstructured" questions in section **038**. Now think about your class in offbeat ways.
   WRITE an "offbeat" question (and an offbeat answer) about a person in your class.
   WRITE another offbeat question (and answer) about (1) a place in your class, (2) an object in your class, (3) an issue or event in your class, (4) a process in your class, and (5) a story, or narrative, you connect with your class.

Through Different Lenses .... *Writing About Experiences*   D

■ Review the sections on "Writing About Experiences" (**144-149**).
   CHOOSE an experience you've always wanted to tell about.
   TURN to the list of "Writing Forms" in section **041**.
   CHOOSE one writing form from two of the four categories: personal writing, creative writing, subject writing, or persuasive writing.
   WRITE two versions of your experience, each in a different form.

What's in a name? .... *The Personal Essay* A

■ If you've been told to write about a personal experience but can't think of anything to write, read the "Helpful Hint" in section **046**.

Here's a twist on that activity that might work for you:

WRITE the letters of your own name in a vertical column down the left side of your page. Skip lines between letters. Then,

LIST at least two topics suggested by each letter.

Rewards and Punishments........................ *Personalizing the School Essay* B

■ Say you've been asked to write on a traditional topic, like "An experience that changed my life." How can you make it interesting?

TURN to *Write Source 2000*, section **058**. FOCUS on the second suggestion. Now try this variation on that suggestion:

START writing your essay (just the beginning). As you write, IMAGINE that a huge alligator is chasing you with a gaping mouth full of gleaming white teeth. Only a slender stick props open its jaws. If you write a single sentence that is boring, ordinary, or useless, the stick will SNAP and the alligator will bite you in the rump!

Now START your essay a different way. Begin with a different first word and go on. This time, IMAGINE that for every clear, lively, and personally interesting sentence you write, you will receive a $45 gift certificate from your favorite store.

CHOOSE the beginning you like better and keep it going.

A Leap of Dolphins .... *Agreement with Collective Nouns* C

■ Use the table in the "Student Almanac" portion of *Write Source 2000* (**797**) to find out the collective nouns for different kinds of animals.

PICK OUT a collective noun that sounds new and interesting to you, and use that noun as the subject of two sentences.

WRITE the first sentence using a singular verb.

WRITE the second sentence using a plural verb. (Be sure your sentences make logical sense.) You'll find advice on singular and plural verbs with collective nouns in section **097**.

For an extra challenge, THINK up an imaginative, new, descriptive-sounding collective noun: for example, a butt of goats or a leap of dolphins.

Less is more. .... *Improving Your Writing* A

■ Don't miss the good advice in section **121**: "Don't use two words—a verb and an adverb—when a single, vivid verb would be better." Read sections **119-121** to understand how to write more vividly and economically. Then study these samples:

The architect *carefully looked over* the blueprints.

The architect **scanned** the blueprints.

The architect **poured over** the blueprints.

That mutt *ran away with* my burrito.

That mutt **filched** my burrito.

Now you TRY IT:

The loaded bleachers *gave out a high-pitched creaking sound.*

The neighborhood mail carrier always *said things under his breath* to passersby.

Diet Plan .... *Improving Your Writing* B

■ Section **123** helps you spot any major weaknesses in your writing. Browse through the five points, but settle on No. 5.

PRACTICE fixing sentences that start with the empty words "There" or "It." For example, this sentence needs some "fat reduction":

There was a bloodthirsty mosquito that got into my bedroom last night.

To fix it: (1) Take out "There," (2) Take out the empty verb "was," (3) Take out the word "that," (4) Use "mosquito" as your new subject, (5) Choose a new verb (or use "got") and rebuild the sentence around it.

A bloodthirsty mosquito sneaked into my bedroom last night.

Now USE this same approach to reduce the fat in the following sentences:

It was a passing fire engine that made me swallow my friendship ring.

At last there were some decent cereals that showed up in our cupboard.

There was this bigger kid who stole Trevor's hightops.

Journey to the Center of the Problem .... *Personal Research* C

■ Read and enjoy the *Write Source 2000* tips on doing "Personal Research" (**265-270**). Pay special attention to the four points under "Connecting: Telling Your Research Story" (**270**).

REMEMBER a time in your life when you discovered something for yourself by tracking down the answer, maybe by talking to other people or by reading a book or magazine.

JOT DOWN whatever you remember that fits under the four headings: (1) What I Knew, (2) What I Wanted to Know, (3) What I Found Out, and (4) What I Learned.

Between Covers .... *Parts of a Book*

■ Review the description of "Parts of a Book" in section **301**.
STUDY the parts and organization of *Write Source 2000*.
LIST on the left side of a piece of paper each part that you are able to find in *Write Source 2000*.
LIST other parts you found in *Write Source 2000* that are not mentioned in **301** on the right.

Tale, Legend, or Lie? .... *Using the Thesaurus*

■ Read the instructions for "Using the Thesaurus" in section **302**.
CHOOSE one of the following pairs of words: find/lose, sober/drunk, build/destroy.
LOOK UP both words in a thesaurus and
STUDY the kinds of words listed under each one.
WRITE a paragraph explaining the difference you notice between the language we use for something good and for something bad.

My Last Bright Idea .... *Creative Process* C

■ When was the last time you had a creative idea that you turned into a project?
WRITE down all that you can remember about how the idea first came to you, how it developed, and what you did with it.
COMPARE your experience of the creative process with the notes on the creative process that you will find in sections **335-342**. What are the differences? What new ideas did you discover in this section? How would you describe the creative process in general?

Fuzzball .... *Avoid Fuzzy Thinking*

■ Sections **350-355** demonstrate six kinds of fuzzy thinking you should avoid in your writing. FORM a group of three students and DECIDE which of the six kinds of fuzziness shows up in these sentences:

Don't worry about wearing a bicycle helmet—millions of bicyclists don't.

We've had rain two days in a row.
Looks like the drought is finally going to end.

The judge ought to give the sex offender a break because
that's the American way.

If you're nicely warmed up now, CHALLENGE another group to a game of "Fuzzball."
❑ In this game, your team makes up a sentence that demonstrates one of the six kinds of fuzzy thinking. The other side guesses which one it is. Back and forth you go. MAKE UP your own rules for scoring.

Look around. .... *Context Clues* A

■ USE the context clues listed in section **370** to figure out the meaning of the unusual underlined words in the following sentences:
  1. Like all <u>marsupials,</u> the kangaroo carries its babies in a pouch.
  2. She went to a kidney specialist because she feared <u>renal</u> failure.
  3. Unlike the milder penalties for shoplifting, this one seemed <u>draconian.</u>
  4. That boy has a <u>gargantuan</u> appetite: he gets two helpings for himself, then finishes everyone else's plate, and finally orders dessert.
  5. A mechanic at the garage inspected the truck's drive shaft, <u>universal joint,</u> and rear axle.
  WRITE DOWN your definition of each word and compare yours with someone else's, or consult a dictionary.

Subjects and Kinds................................. *Kinds of Literature* B

■ In sections **041** and **385** you will find handy lists of many of the types of literature. Look them over carefully.
  On your own paper, WRITE the numbers 1 through 7, one for each of the subjects listed below.
  After each number, LIST two or three kinds of literature from the handbook lists which would seem like good forms to use for writing about that subject:
  1. A teenage girl argues with her mother
  2. How clocks were invented
  3. A great queen dies after she trusts a dishonest advisor
  4. The problems a family faces after a burglar enters their home
  5. Aliens haunt a family's old vacation home
  6. A day when everything goes wrong for a kid who thinks he's the handsomest kid in school
  7. The beauty of sunlight on the sailboats in an ocean harbor

The plot thickens. .... *Plot* C

■ Pick out any portion of your life that seemed to have a natural starting point, a development of some kind, and an ending of some sort. (For example, you met a kid at Camp Wa-Pa-Toot-See who acted mean but saved you from drowning and then became your friend.)
  MAKE a list down the left side of your page of the five steps in a typical plot line. (See **386**.)
  After each step, JOT DOWN all your memories of the episode you've chosen which seem to fit under that heading.
  When you're finished, WRITE down your thoughts on whether or not your experience took the shape of the "average" plot. **Pay special attention** to the differences.

© 1995 Write Source Educational Publishing House, Box 460, Burlington, WI 53105

Mind if I tape this? .... *Interviewing/Creative Collaboration*

■ Study the sections on "Interviewing" (**405-407**).
  ASK your friend to PRETEND to be someone he or she always dreamed of being. Your friend should try to imagine as much as possible about what that person's life is like.
  PUT ON your best interviewing behavior and interview your friend.
  WRITE out the best questions you can think of—the kind the interviewee is best prepared to answer and the kind that will pique other people's interest.
  BE PREPARED to go beyond your written questions as the interview develops.

Let's be objective about this. ....*Taking Objective Tests* B

■ STUDY the tips on answering objective test questions in sections **428-431**.
  Next, READ the one-paragraph essay answer about Hiroshima in section **425**.
  Finally, using the information in that paragraph as the material for a "quiz," COMPOSE a true/false test question, a matching test question, a multiple-choice question, and a fill-in-the-blanks question.

Goal to Go .... *Goal Setting*

■ In the section on "Individual Skills" (**450-457**), read with special care about "Setting Goals" (**450-451**). On paper,
  WRITE DOWN one major goal for your **life**.
  WRITE DOWN a goal for **next year** to help you achieve the one above.
  WRITE DOWN a goal for **next week** to help you achieve the one above.
  WRITE DOWN a goal for **tomorrow** to help you achieve the one above.
  WRITE DOWN a goal for **tonight** to help you achieve the one above.
  WRITE DOWN a goal for **next hour** to help you achieve the one above.

911 .... *Using Ellipses* D

■ You're a news reporter sent to cover a fire in a nearby apartment house.
  WRITE down an exact transcription (word-for-word record) of the fire chief who is describing how firefighters rescued five children from the burning building.
  After checking topic numbers **464-467**, USE ellipses correctly in your transcription.

Broken Reply .... *Using Ellipses*

■ Study the guidelines for using ellipses (**465-467**).
  REMEMBER (or imagine) a time when you broke something valuable that belonged to someone else.
  SUPPOSE the owner asks, in pain or in anger, "How did *this* happen?"
  WRITE a broken reply, using ellipses correctly to show pauses and missing words.

Stand-Up Commas .... *Commas Separating Adjectives*   A

■ PRINT the following adjectives on six separate signs (8½- x 11-inch or larger):

woolly	expensive	fancy
thick	mohair	turtleneck

PRINT another sign with the word "sweater" on it and two or three more with big, bold commas (,).

GIVE the word cards to one team and the comma cards to another team. Now,

LET the members of the first team stand up in front to form a phrase including the word "sweater" and more than one adjective.

IF a comma is necessary between adjectives, LET a "comma" go up and stand between the "adjectives."

SWITCH teams and challenge each other.

SCORE the game any way you like.

And Now, for a Short Pause .... *Semicolons and Colons*   B

■ Do you often confuse semicolons with colons? Many people do. Turn to *Write Source 2000*, sections **484-493**, for a review of the basic rules.

READ each of the following sentences.

NOTE how a semicolon or colon is used in it.

In the blank space, WRITE down the number of the section in the handbook that states the rule for that sentence.

_____ 1. The stench in our garden arose from three things: my brother's discarded lobster shells, our cat's little "gifts," and some rotting fruit that fell from a gingko tree.

_____ 2. The hang-glider pilot sucked up a deep breath before takeoff; he looked scared.

_____ 3. The Berlin Wall came down in November 1989; however, it was months before the unification of the two Germanies became official.

_____ 4. The cafeteria served up some very interesting food: Twinkies, HoHos, and DingDongs; sandwiches, buns, and rolls made of the spongiest imaginable white bread; and watered-down grape juice.

Traveling Lightly .... *Using Semicolons*   C

■ Suppose you are going camping and you want to pack all of the following groups of items:

dried apples, chocolate drink mix, and powdered eggs
camp stools, a folding shovel, and a gas lantern
a water kettle, a no-stick frying pan, a plastic dishpan,
and a pair of cloth dish towels

INCLUDE all these items in one long sentence about your camping trip.

USE semicolons correctly in the series (see **487**).

Keeku! Keeku! .... *Using Semicolons*

- Study the guidelines for using semicolons (**483-487**).
  READ "Fashionation" (**141**).
  FIND two sentences which use semicolons; REWRITE the independent clauses in
    them as separate sentences so that semicolons are no longer needed.
  FIND two other pairs of sentences that could be joined with a semicolon; JOIN them,
    punctuating correctly.

Superduperphone .... *Using the Dash* B

- Read the model sentence about the "superphone" of the future in section **495**.
  NOTICE how dashes are used in it.
    IMAGINE an even wilder kind of phone in the further distant future.
    DESCRIBE your "superduperphone" in sentences modeled after the ones in **495**. Be
      sure to use the dash correctly.

Word Factory .... *Using Hyphens*

- Find the descriptive phrases *following* the verbs in the two sentences below.
  REWRITE the sentences so that each descriptive phrase becomes a "one-word" adjec-
    tive, an adjective which appears *before* the noun it is describing. Use hyphens to
    combine the adjectives into one word as shown in the sample sentence. (See **505**
    for help.)
  Descriptive Phrase: We passed a car *covered with snow* stranded in the ditch.
  One-word Adjective: We passed a *snow-covered* car stranded in the ditch.

      Tarumi bought a Halloween costume *sewn by hand.*
      On my head I have a parakeet *born in the jungle.*

You don't have to shout! .... *Using Exclamation Points*

- Suppose you're sitting in a doctor's office when somebody suddenly walks in the door
  and begins describing an accident that just took place down the street.
    WRITE down what that person says, using exclamation points.
    Now WRITE down the same words, but drop the exclamation points.
    Finally, WRITE down your comments about how you would feel in those two differ-
      ent situations—how you would feel about the speaker, what you would feel like
      doing in response, what you would say in return, etc.
  The comments in section **510** may give you some valuable advice.

Pssst! .... *Using Quotation Marks*   A

■ Study the guidelines for using double and single quotation marks (**511-515**).
REMEMBER something you said earlier today (or earlier this year).
IMAGINE you overhear two people gossiping about you. (Where are they? How do
  they know you? What is their attitude toward you?) One is telling the other what
  you said, using your exact words.
WRITE down their conversation exactly, using double and single quotation marks.

So to Speak .... *Using Quotation Marks*   B

■ Study guideline **516** for using quotation marks.
THINK of a distinctive slang word which one of your friends always uses.
WRITE a sentence about your friend, using the word in a special way.
USE quotation marks properly to draw attention to the special use.

The Hess Family .... *Forming Possessives*   C

■ Say there was a family in your town named Hess. There was the dad, Les, the
mother, Bess, Aunt Jess, the daughter, Tess, big brother Fess, and a naughty little boy
they nicknamed "Mess." Oh, and a three-legged poodle named Wes. A tornado came
while they were on vacation. Now they're back, sorting through the rubble where their
house once stood.
WRITE your imaginative version of their comments as they sort through the rubble,
  picking up and identifying different items that belong to members of their family.
USE apostrophes correctly to form singular and plural possessives, following the
  guidelines in sections **522-524**.

Divided Attention .... *Using Parentheses*   D

■ Suppose you were asked to visit a PTA meeting and talk to the parents about
something exciting you've done in one of your classes lately. Only one problem—down
in the front three rows sit about 15 kindergartners who've been asked to sing. You
have to toss in some words of explanation on the side so they won't get bored or
confused.
WRITE your speech, using parentheses according to the guidelines in **532** to show
  the comments tossed in for the sake of the kindergartners.

Double Vision .... *Forming Plural Nouns*   E

■ Study the guidelines for forming plural nouns (**547-554**).
SUPPOSE you are attending a convention of twins; you and your twin are talking
  with another pair of twins about what a pain it is to buy two of everything.
WRITE your conversation in the form of a play script (see **260** for a model), using as
  many different kinds of plurals as you can.

Ice cube rides again. .... *Spelling*

■ Turn to the "Yellow Pages Guide to Improved Spelling" (**568-573**).
  PICK OUT **one word** that is very hard for you to learn to spell: "icicle," for example.
  FIGURE OUT the letter that gives you the most trouble. Maybe you always forget whether the third letter is a "y" or an "i." Mentally VISUALIZE the "i."
  Now, MAKE a weird picture suggested by the word—"icicle" could bring to mind an "ice cube" riding on a "bicycle."
  Now, WORK the difficult letter into the picture somehow—for example, put a big letter "I" in a basket of the bike which is being pedaled by the ice cube.
  Finally, DRAW A PICTURE of the weird scene you've imagined, and let that picture remind you of the proper spelling. TRY this technique on some other hard words. HAVE FUN!

Door Jam.......................... *Spotting Subjects and Predicates*

■ Study the sections on subjects and predicates (**696-705**).
  READ the story in section **401** about the girl who lost her fingernail playing "chicken."
  LIST on a separate sheet the simple subject and simple predicate in each sentence.
  PUT a star next to the five most effective subjects and predicates.

The Big S................................. *Identifying Complete Subjects*

■ In sections **697-700** of the "Yellow Pages," you will find short descriptions of simple, complete, and compound subjects.
  FIND the **complete subject** ("The Big S") in each of the following sentences. WRITE each one down. (*Note:* They get a little harder as they go along.)

Movies and tortilla chips kept Tony awake all night.

A little piece of New York died with him.

America's most distinctive moviemaker had directed just four features in a 15-year career.

A fortune in natural pearls comes from pearl beds off the western coast of Australia.

Give me your address before you leave.

From the common, or European, pear have come such familiar varieties as Bartlett, Comice, Anjou, Bosc, Dana Hovey, Hardy, Seckel, and Winter Nelis.

The Big P .... *Identifying Complete Predicates* | A

■ In sections **701-705** of the "Yellow Pages," you will find short descriptions of simple, complete, and compound predicates.
   FIND the **complete predicate** ("The Big P") in each of the following sentences.
   WRITE each one down. (*Note:* They get a little harder as they go along.)

My fat, bossy aunt from Minneapolis always borrows my watch.

He chuckled and nonchalantly handed me one program.

*Ear-piercing noise suddenly bursts out of the amps and
into the stale, smokey air.*

*In The Right Stuff, author Tom Wolfe tells the story of the test pilots who
risked their lives breaking the sound barrier during the late forties.*

Send me about four boxes of those.

Did you hear that?............................... *Identifying Modifiers* | B

■ After you study the comments on phrases in sections **708-709**, READ the following sentence:

*In the cluttered, overheated space Juan called his office, at least one of us
thought he heard a faint whimper, as if a child had mistakenly crawled
into a locking file cabinet drawer and were feebly calling for help.*

LIST the modifying words or phrases you find in this sentence; place each one in one
   of the categories below:
   · Word modifying a noun   · Word modifying a verb
   · Word modifying a modifier   · Phrase modifying a noun
   · Phrase modifying a verb

The Four Stooges on Venus..................... *Kinds of Sentences* | C

■ Study the four different kinds of sentences described in **715-718**.
   CREATE four characters—four "stooges"—one who speaks only in *declarative* sentences, another only in *interrogatives*, another only in *imperatives*, and another only in *exclamations*.
   WRITE a short, funny radio drama about the "Four Stooges" as they step out of their Venusian Landing Vehicle (VLV) onto the planet's surface. (Keep each of the stooges in character.)
   HINT: You'll have more to work with if you first study what scientists already know about the atmosphere on Venus.

Lost and Found (I) .... *Identifying Types of Nouns*   **A**

■ Study the definitions and examples of types of nouns in **719-724**.

On a sheet of paper, MAKE three headings: "Concrete Nouns," "Abstract Nouns," and "Collective Nouns."

READ the fascinating biography of Francis Ann Slocum in section **157**.

LIST all the concrete nouns in the biography under the proper heading; do the same for abstract and collective nouns.

PLACE a "c" in parentheses after the word if it is a common noun and a "p" if it is proper.

Lost and Found (II) .... *Identifying Pronouns and Antecedents*   **B**

■ Review personal pronouns and antecedents in **733-735**.

READ once again the story of Francis Slocum's life among the Miami Indians (**157**).

LIST all the personal pronouns you can find.

After each pronoun, add a dash and write the antecedent (if you can find one).

And on Your Left .... *Kinds of Pronouns*   **C**

■ Review the "Other Types of Pronouns" (besides personal pronouns) in **743-748**; notice the helpful chart after **748**.

Now SUPPOSE you landed a job as a tour guide who has to show international visitors all the fascinating sights in your own bedroom. It's your first day of work and you need to practice.

WRITE down a first draft of your spiel.

USE at least one of each kind of pronoun—relative, demonstrative, interrogative, intensive, reflexive, and indefinite.

TRADE papers with someone and challenge him or her to find an example of each different kind of pronoun.

Beyond Awesome, Different, and Cool .... *Degrees of Adjectives and Adverbs*   **D**

■ Study the positive, comparative, and superlative forms of adjectives (**779-784**) and adverbs (**787**).

THINK of three different things to compare—three roller coasters, three movies, three flavors of pizza, etc.—where one seems good, another better, and the third best (or bad, worse, and worst).

SUPPOSE one friend describes the three things as "awesome, more awesome, and most awesome"; another retorts, "No man, they are cool, cooler, and coolest!"

Not satisfied, you WRITE your own critique of the three.

USE the three degrees of adjectives and adverbs effectively in your critique.

Three Bears .... *Forms of Adjectives*   A

■ The three bears, after they ran away from Goldilocks' house, started arguing over which one of them was the least, the middle, and the most of all sorts of things. So they made a chart, like this:

	Baby Bear	Mama Bear	Daddy Bear
fat	**fat**	**fatter**	**fattest**
hungry			
ridiculous			
clever			
good			

MAKE your own chart like this on a piece of paper and fill it in with positive, comparative, and superlative forms of the adjectives you choose.
If you need help with the forms, check out sections **779-784** in the "Yellow Pages."

Heads and Tails .... *Prepositions*   B

■ Read the definitions of prepositions and prepositional phrases in sections **788-790**. NOTE the table of prepositions on the same page.
PICK OUT a handful of prepositions from the list.
For each preposition you choose, MAKE UP two sentences, one with the preposition in a phrase at the *beginning* of the sentence and one with the preposition in a phrase at the *end*.
If you would like, FOCUS all your sentences on the same topic or MAKE them add up to a story.

Wow! What? Phew! Oh? .... *Duolog and Interjections*   C

■ Study the brief description of interjections in **791**.
WRITE a duolog (see **254**) in which your two characters speak *only* in interjections.
WRITE one version with stage directions (see **260**) and another without.
GIVE your version without stage directions to another person to see if he or she can figure out what's happening. Help each other improve the scripts.

It Changed the World. .... *Using Time Lines*   D

■ Refer to "Historical Time Line" in your handbook (**889-898**).
SELECT and study any 50-year period in history.
LIST the five most important events, from your point of view, that occurred during this period of time.
Then WRITE a paragraph explaining the importance of one of the events.

Graphic Designer .... *Using Graphs*   A

■ Study the section on graphs in your handbook (**813-817**).
THINK of information in your life such as interests, hobbies, collections, and so on, that could be presented in a graph.
CHOOSE the right type of graph to display this information. (*The number of books you have read this year* could be displayed in a **line graph**. *The number of books you have read compared to the number read by a few of your classmates* could be displayed in a **bar graph**.)
Then CREATE your graph.

Presidential Happenings ..... *Using Tables and Time Lines*   B

■ Survey the "U.S. Presidents and Vice Presidents" table in your handbook (**880**).
LIST the name of one of the presidents and the years he was in office.
Then REFER to the "Historical Time Line" section of the handbook (**889-898**).
STUDY the years the president you have chosen was in office.
WRITE a paragraph about this president focusing on the information in the time line.

Up from Number 2 .... *Using Tables*   C

■ Study the "U.S. Presidents and Vice Presidents" table in your handbook (**880**).
LIST all of the vice presidents who went on to become president.
NAME the one individual from this list who did not immediately move from the office of vice president to the office of president.
IDENTIFY two other pieces of information that you can learn from this list. (For example, how many vice presidents became presidents because their predecessors did not finish their terms in office?)

Two is company. .... *Using Time Lines*   D

■ Survey the "Historical Time Line" (**889-898**).
CHOOSE two different people from the Historical Time Line you would like to know more about.
READ about these two individuals in encyclopedia articles. (Take brief notes as you read.)
WRITE a sentence that would make an interesting comparison between these two people.

Special Challenge: Write a comparison/contrast paragraph about your two subjects.

Taking Root .... *Using Roots* A

- Find the section on "Roots" in your handbook (**378**).
  SELECT a root that has at least two different forms. For example: *flex, flect*
  WRITE a sentence or two that include words with each of these roots. Make your
    sentences interesting, as if they were part of a story.
  For example: When he re<u>flect</u>ed on the accident, he remembered the fear of discover-
    ing his elbow was totally in<u>flex</u>ible.
  UNDERLINE the roots of your two words.
  EXCHANGE your sentence(s) with a classmate.
  CHECK your handbook and a dictionary to see if the underlined words are used
    correctly.

Life Lines .... *Writing to Learn* B

- Read "You can learn about LIFE through writing" (**010**) in your handbook.
  CONSIDER what has set you thinking lately. It could be something you saw, heard,
    read, or experienced in the world around you.
  WRITE about what you saw, heard, read, or experienced as a journal entry.
  LABEL your finished entry with one word that states the importance of the experi-
    ence. Maybe it has to do with *fame, fear, health, hope,* or *opportunity*?

Follow Through .... *Setting Goals* C

- Read the first page of "Setting Goals" in your handbook (**450**).
  DECIDE on one goal that you would like to set for yourself, and record it on the top
    of your paper.
  NOW READ "Guidelines for Setting Goals" (**451**).
  WRITE a sentence for each guideline explaining how you plan to meet it. (The first
    guideline reminds you to "Be realistic . . ." So, your first sentence would explain
    why you believe your goal is one you can actually expect to achieve.)

A Stress Test .... *Managing Stress* D

- Turn to "Managing Stress" (**455-457**) in your handbook.
  REVIEW the "Causes of Stress" list (**445**).
  SELECT one area of stress that you have experienced.
  READ the section on "Reducing Stress" (**457**).
  WRITE about how you might apply one of the three approaches to your stressful
    situation.